COLIN TURNER

SECRET

SERVICE

LICENCE TO THRILL

YOUR CUSTOMERS

21st
Century
Books

First Published in Europe in 2009 by
21st Century Books (UK) Ltd
Canterbury

British Library Cataloguing
Publication Data available

ISBN: 978-1-904956-24-2

Printed and Bound in Great Britain
By CPI Antony Rowe
Chippenham and Eastbourne

SECRET SERVICE

LICENCE TO THRILL
YOUR CUSTOMERS

Described by *Time* as '*a leading authority on business*' and referred to by *Business Age* as '*Europe's foremost teacher for success*;' Colin Turner is the bestselling author of 15 books published in 45 countries and 39 languages, with two million enjoyed by readers. His books and audio programs instrumental in developing leading businesses and individuals are available from www.colinturner.com

CONTENTS

PREFACE

This is the story of an aspiring agent's mission to escape the State of Mediocrity and reach Service City, the Capital of Prosperity.

There will be many challenges ahead, but if successful the aspiring agent will become a top operative within the Secret Service. An Agency that is essential to the success of the whole of Prosperity and to its valued Founder, known as Customer.

According to the State of Mediocrity's definition of success, aspiring agent Smith is a good example. After earning an average degree at University, he got an average job with an average company.

Because he works hard he was appointed Director of Customer Service at his firm, Communication Limited. It is at this point that he begins to feel a gnawing frustration. This is where our story begins...

Escape from the State of Mediocrity

'TAKE A SEAT,' COMMANDED RECEPTIONIST robotically, with a cursory glance, before returning to her computer. 'I'll be with you in a minute.' Her second glance to confirm her instructions had been carried out turned to one of horror, as she could not believe her eyes. 'Excuse me!'

Smith was not sure what had come over him; perhaps it was the final straw in recent events that had caused him to lose faith in society, but at that moment he decided to follow Receptionist's instruction precisely. He literally picked up one of the chairs in the waiting area and began to walk out with it. 'Ah!' said Smith, 'I have your attention. I was wondering what I had do to get some service.'

Receptionist's eyes narrowed. She may have been caught off guard but there was no way she was going to allow *anyone* to query the autocracy with which she clearly ruled her domain. 'This is a Legal Department,' she answered slowly, ' we don't serve, we sue.'

What is it about certain receptionists, thought Smith. Wasn't it their job to welcome people? He noticed the framed Mission Statement hanging on the wall. The message was highly commendable yet the part: *committed to serve our clients*, seemed incongruent with Receptionist's behaviour. She was the 'shop window' of the office, the point of first call, a client's first experience of the company she represented. Had she bought into

1

what was hanging on the wall? Had she even been involved in its creation?

Perhaps the answer was in the second part of that statement: *to the best of our abilities*. People's best abilities had obviously not been fully developed here. Or was it him? Perhaps *their* attitude was right and it was *him* that was being difficult.

Recently Smith had been trying to work out whether those people who had served him had actually enjoyed the opportunity to be of service. He had come to the conclusion that they served because they *had* to, because it was their job. Not because they wanted to, or chose to. Certainly they did not seem to *enjoy* it.

'So, do you *have* an appointment?' asked Receptionist forcing herself to be pleasant, while once more scanning her screen in anticipation for the automated answer, one that should now come her way, as it always did from people who entered her domain.

Smith dutifully answered aware that Receptionist was confirming it on the screen in front of her. There was a change in her tone when she realised that it was a Senior Partner he was visiting, and that they were having lunch together.

'Take a se…. I'll let Lawyer know that you are here…you shouldn't have to wait long.'

Why should Receptionist become more pleasant because of *who* he was seeing, thought Smith. What difference should that make? Yet clearly it made her more amenable to him. Or was she more concerned that Smith would report the exchange to her boss *before* she was able.

❑   ❑   ❑

'YOU'LL LIKE THIS RESTAURANT,' said Lawyer. 'It's very exclusive.'

'And the service too, no doubt,' replied Smith.

'Eh? Yes of course – particularly if you're a regular patron. You go in and I'll join you in a moment, just got to wash my hands.'

Smith walked up to the reservation gate and stood by the sign: 'wait to be seated'. Why couldn't it read 'please wait to be greeted', or 'please let us guide you to your table', at least something more welcoming thought Smith. A moment later Maitre' D appeared and asked for Smith's name, rank and number, to which Smith responded obediently, although reluctantly. By now Smith had realised that to do anything other than 'as he was told' would compromise what Maitre' D saw as the security of his position and probably delay lunch.

During the meal Smith occasionally watched the waiters, particularly when other diners were attempting to catch their attention – or any waiter for that matter. He noticed that some of the waiters had mastered the art of ignoring the customer desperate to attract attention. Delivering a particular dish to a specific table, the waiters did not want to be waylaid, especially if the table was not within their specified area. They almost seemed to sense when a diner wanted to attract their attention, and become even more elusive. Surely it was not possible to avoid gazes, in the way that they did, without consciously trying?

For the second time today Smith wondered if the staff had chosen to work here, were forced into it, or were simply waiting for something else to come up. It was quite clear to see which waiters enjoyed what they did, those that did not, and the ones who were just biding their time.

3

'You seem weighed down with the world's problems, anything bothering you?' enquired Lawyer.

'Do you ever phone your own office?' asked Smith as if in reply.

'Eh? What do you mean? Of course I do, doesn't everyone some time or other?' answered Lawyer, puzzled.

'I mean the main number, the same one that your clients, your customers, have to phone?'

'Of course not,' he retorted, 'If I need to speak to anyone, or get messages I phone my assistant on her direct line, same as you do, no doubt.'

'And leave a message on her voice mail?' enquired Smith further.

'If she's not there, which is more often the case than not, come to think of it since we had the system installed by your people,' replied Lawyer.

'But have you *any* idea how your prospective and existing clients are greeted when they first phone or even visit your firm?'

❏   ❏   ❏

SMITH DID NOT RETURN TO HIS OFFICE immediately, instead he headed for the Park. He needed time to think as his head was pounding with frustration. Perhaps he was worried because, as Customer Service Director responsible for his company's future success, his awareness of service had changed. He was becoming more aware that good service did not exist. Even the Park signs told you what you *couldn't* do. No litter; Keep off the grass. They never invited what you were *able* to do, like please keep to the paths. Smith realised that all the service he had personally experienced had been half-hearted and completely without good will.

4

On the way to his lunch he had been forced to take the Taxi he didn't want, a grimy cab, the driver smoking. He had gone to the clean non-smoking second in line and had been told that he must take the first in line. You're paying for a ride, not the quality of the vehicle, you know, Driver had quipped unpleasantly, before blowing smoke. The trip had been uncomfortable as Driver had an aggressive attitude to traffic while continually speaking on his mobile telephone.

Nearing Smith's destination Driver had said, "The address is down a one way street so it'll be easier to drop you here, mate." Easier for whom, thought Smith, me? Why was it that Driver was making out he had done Smith a huge favour, as he looked expectantly for a tip when Smith, the customer, paid the fare?

The chances of Smith being obliged to say 'thanks for the ride,' were infinitely greater than receiving a 'thanks for your custom.' But then he wasn't perceived as a *real* customer; he was only a passenger who was lucky enough to find an empty cab. Yes, he had been taken for a ride, and for how long had he. Why did he feel conditioned to give a tip, even when he didn't feel justified in doing so?

Earlier that morning he had phoned the call centre of the Firm he worked for: Communication Limited. The centre had been set up to deal with customer complaints. After an endless series of electronic options he heard discordant music interrupted periodically with a request to hold as that the call was important to them. Finally his call was answered.

'Hello', said Smith. 'That took a long time.'

'Well, we're very busy today,' replied a voice before adding, 'What's your reference number?'

Smith dutifully answered only to be told that the computers were 'down' and perhaps Smith could call back later.

'Then why did you ask for my reference number?' asked Smith, too late as his call had already been disconnected.

Later, at an electronic goods store he had enquired about ipods. Waiting for a few moments at the counter, he noticed that Assistant was busily attending to a product display by the door. A display obviously intended to attract customers, thought Smith. He could hear two other assistants chatting together, hidden by the partition beyond the counter.

He knew that Assistant had noticed him, but it was apparent that he was hoping to finish what he started. Smith was sure he heard him mumble, 'How can I be expected to finish this product display to attract customers when I am continually interrupted by them?' Finally, seeing that no one would be coming to Smith's assistance, Assistant got up, looked at him, and said, 'Yes.'

'I was wondering if you could tell me the difference between these two players,' asked Smith

Assistant looked at both the units and after a few moments pointed at one of them. 'That one's the best'

'Why that one?' enquired Smith.

'It's the most expensive,' replied Assistant. 'It'll have a better sound.'

Smith could see that they were different makes, but apart from that they looked identical. 'Why is that exactly?' He asked.

'Don't ask me,' said Assistant, 'I'm only part-time.'

□   □   □

SMITH, REFLECTED THAT THE SERVICE he had experienced was by people *having* to serve him, not wanting to, or even enjoying the opportunity to do so. Service was a job unsupported by either trade or profession.

'Service stinks!' shouted Smith in frustration.

'Not everywhere,' said a voice behind him.

Smith turned in surprise. 'Who are you?'

'Intuition,' came the reply before continuing: 'there is a place where the true meaning of Service is understood. Where people understand that in work you produce something, but through service you *become* someone.'

Smith looked sceptical: 'And where would that be?'

'The Capital of Prosperity where business is loyal to their Founder because it wants to be, not because it has to. There, Customer, that is the name of the Founder, rules and the people enjoy living in Prosperity; and, because the people are prosperous, so is their Founder. His first duty is to be loyal to the people in recognition and reward for their service.'

'It sounds too good to be true. Tell me where it is so I can experience it and judge for myself.'

Intuition looked directly into Smith's eyes. 'Can you rightfully judge another's street, when your own house is in such a State? The mission is challenging and requires a change of thinking.'

'Well, although I would like to believe that a better way of service exists, I have no idea how to go about it,' admitted Smith reluctantly. 'But I am willing to leave the State of Mediocrity, and embark on this mission.'

'Good,' said Intuition, 'because getting to Prosperity involves a mission to learn, understand and apply service secrets that many are either ignorant of, or consider a myth.'

'I am aware that something is wrong,' interrupted Smith. 'That despite initiatives of business to boost growth through emphasis and focus on customer services and marketing, they are still failing to deliver what they promise.'

'There are three stages from unawareness to awareness,' said Intuition. 'First, most individuals and businesses are unaware that they are unaware. Then, as you yourself are now experiencing, they become aware that they *are* unaware. The third stage follows a path consciously chosen, and leads to becoming aware that they *are* aware. This level can only be gained through a personal mission that seeks the development of potential. The marketing initiatives you speak of, for example, are based on a wrong interpretation of marketing. Rather than ask "*who* is our customer and *how* can we deliver what they really want?" Marketing at the moment asks: "how can we sell *more* of what *we* want to sell?"

Smith sighed: 'That's why I am so frustrated. No-one seems to care about anything other than what's in it for them.'

'When you take this mission that frustration will start to fade. You must listen to your initial awareness or your future will be being lost in a State of Mediocrity.'

'OK,' said Smith determinedly. 'How do I start this mission?'

'I would say that *your* mission has already started,' replied Intuition. 'Go directly to Change Border at the edge of this State. Then ask to see Evaluate. Tell him I sent you and answer his questions correctly. If he is able to give you a pass then he will guide you further.'

☐   ☐   ☐

'LOOK SMITH, I HAVEN'T GOT THE TIME FOR THIS,' said Too-Busy. 'We've done the change *and* the mission thing already so I can't see what you're getting so upset about.'

'And, it was expensive,' added Cynical. 'I've never been convinced that any of it was worth the amount of money spent on it. Money that *could* have been utilised elsewhere.'

'But I don't remember any involvement,' returned Smith. 'And apart from a few redundancies, my department didn't notice any change. We still had to follow the same old processes without question. The only difference is that we had a statement for what we aspired to do hanging on the wall.'

'Perhaps you benefited more than you realise,' said Hidden-Agenda. 'After all you are heading that department now, so no complaints in that respect, eh?'

'The point that I'm making,' replied Smith, 'is that we must listen to what our customers want and build our policy and strategy around their wants.'

'That would be economic suicide!' blurted out Cynical. 'Our strategy is based on offering them what *we* have for sale in such an *attractive* way that *they* go ahead and *buy* it. It works.'

'What we're telling them is *not* what we're selling them,' protested Smith.

'Look, everyone knows that the loudest and most frequent voice sells - that's a first rule of marketing, so who cares? And with our products selling as well as they are, we have a good marketing budget to make certain we stay the most often voice heard, don't we? Anyway they can always contact Customer Complaints in your Department, can't they,' continued Hidden Agenda. 'That's a service we specifically set up for them, isn't it?'

'No, it had to be set up to cope with the complaints,' replied Smith. That was the reason. Our policy should be aiming towards fewer complaints, not catering for them. Why can't we aim for *zero defects* by trying to understand what the customer wants?'

'Zero defects?' said Too-Busy. 'It's just not possible in business today, and the time involved is too costly. Who expects it anyway?'

'Would you take a flight if you thought the mechanics of the aircraft did not check out with zero defects?' asked Smith.

'But how do we know for certain that there are zero defects?' answered Cynical. 'If I pull down the table from the seat in front of me during a flight and there's an old coffee stain there, it makes me think what *oil* stains have gone unnoticed in the engine. But surely the reality of today is that people *accept* that what they are told may not be completely backed up. They accept that what they buy will probably not last, or perform as well as they have been led to believe it will.

'People working in the service industry do so for the money, not because they want to. Business is about making profit. And people know that companies are out to make as much as they can. Even if you were successful in developing a strategy for excellent service, how would you get our people to buy into it? To them it would just be yet another strategy and pay it lip service.'

'Of course business must make profit!' shouted Smith. 'That isn't my point, making a profit is what business is about. But I believe that profit should be regarded as the applause for providing good acts of service. So, by providing excellent service we will enjoy the reward of greater applause from our audience. That's the reality!

'All business, and particularly service oriented ones like us, are operating under a false illusion,' continued Smith. 'Business has conditioned itself to believe that customers need business. That's getting it backward. Business needs customers. After all they are the very reason for our existence – without them there would be no revenue, let alone profit! Most people in business do not even know who their prime customer is.'

'So *who* would you consider *yours* to be?' enquired Hidden Agenda.

'The very people who have to follow the strategy and policy that we formulate', answered Smith, 'the employees of course.'

'Our *employees*?' said Cynical in surprise. 'What about our shareholders? We certainly wouldn't be with here without their support. And what about our *paying* customers? Surely they come *before* those people we pay?'

'Every one of our people should be an ambassador of our business and, as such, has a vital role to perform,' said Smith. 'Every ambassador must have the full support of the ruling nation that it represents. Surely our duty is to serve them through training, reward and recognition to the best of our ability so that they in turn can perform with their prime customers, the *paying* ones to coin your phrase, to the best of their ability. Take a ship. When the crew have difficulty with a passenger, and are not certain how to handle them, they seek the captain's advice and support, both in morale and in competency. The captain takes the necessary action that ensures the safety of the vessel that carries the crew and passengers.

'The ship's owner must stand by the captain's decision, whatever it may be, because it is the captain's style of leadership that they invested in to obtain the best return. The captain serves his crew best when he is on the bridge overseeing operations, not while he is in his cabin. Any crewmember, *or* passenger, can speak to the captain should either consider it appropriate.'

'Well, I certainly haven't got the time to speak to every employee,' said Too-Busy. 'And the nature of our work is such that I don't have the time to tittle-tattle with customers. We have a *huge* call centre that spends all day communicating with customers. We have a Human Resources department for our people. No, as far as I'm concerned my prime customers are our major shareholders and with a possible profits warning coming up next quarter I want to keep on the right side of them – we may need extra support.

'Smith, enough of your ideas on better *service*; what we need from you is some ideas to improve *sales*.'

❑   ❑   ❑

'WHAT GOOD WILL RESIGNING DO?' asked Mrs Smith. 'You've only just got to the position where you can make a difference. You're not just shying away from the responsibility of what's ahead of you are you?'

'Certainly, the job has opened my eyes to the poor level of service that our customers have to put up with,' agreed Smith, 'but because of the constraints hidden within established processes and policy, the job may as well be in title only. It's responsibility without power, which is ironic because in my experience most people want power without the responsibility that command brings. That is not the case with me. I feel that I am compromising what I believe to be right, by not delivering what marketing invites and sales promise.'

'Well, I really don't see what you're so frustrated about. We have a home, two children and friends – why risk losing what we have worked so hard for, just because you're all fired up by some *stranger*.

'I don't, but I want to feel a greater sense of fulfilment in what I do. There must be more to life than just *doing to get by*. And if you're referring to my meeting with Intuition,' said Smith, 'he seemed more like a long lost friend, than some stranger, as you suggest. His guidance made sound sense.'

'OK, then as you're always saying that the best ideas are always made outside of the office, make it your mission to find out about this Secret Service you've heard about. If what you have heard is true then everyone will benefit, including Communication Limited.'

□   □   □

IT DID NOT TAKE SMITH LONG TO ORGANISE himself for the mission. Hidden-Agenda did not seem too concerned about Smith's plan to seek further information on how they could increase profits. Moreover, he seemed quite pleased that Smith would be leaving. Cynical had his doubts that whatever Smith returned with, if he did in fact return, would be of any use and Too-Busy ratified the trip only on the basis that Smith took the mission on his own time.

'You're due a vacation, so take it how you want,' he had said. 'Mission indeed! I'm sure that market research can be done from the office. Prove that it works and then we can talk about it *not* being *your* holiday.'

Smith set off in the direction that Intuition had earlier advised, and where he would meet Evaluate at Change Border. He soon noticed two colleagues hurrying after him, Indecisive and Fixed-Thinking.

'So you're really as serious as they say you are?' asked Indecisive.

'Yes, I'm absolutely serious,' replied Smith.

'Then you are as crazy as they say you are!' said Indecisive. 'The grass may appear greener to you elsewhere, but let me tell you, it's just as hard to cut. Our State may be laid back, but who cares, if everyone's content with the way it is?'

'Laid back?' replied Smith, 'this State is more than that! Our service is non-existent and our attitude to service is apathetic. Such a city will not survive in the new era that is coming.'

'What new era?' asked Indecisive.

'A new era of customer focused service, where customers are discerning, know what they want, and will have the power to make or break businesses by their choices.'

'That's ridiculous,' said Fixed-Thinking. 'There will always be customers for the products and service that businesses sell them. Admittedly some are *difficult*, but there are always plenty more to take their place if they don't want to buy.'

'People are not machines,' said Smith. 'People are becoming increasingly wanting to know that they *count* for something, instead of being counted as statistics. The best way to serve yourself is through serving others, but because I do not know how to go about such a thing, I am embarking on a mission that leads to Service City in Prosperity. Why don't you both accompany me?'

'Accompany you?' repeated Fixed-Thinking with a hint of contempt in his voice. 'No way! I'm keeping my feet firmly on this ground that I know. It stops your head from staying in the clouds where some people insist on being. I'm off! Serving *others* indeed, whatever next,' and pulling Indecisive to one side added, 'being with him will not do us any good – his days are numbered. Come on.'

Indecisive paused and said, 'No, I'm not sure. Perhaps our colleague could be on to something here. What if this place he knows about *does* offer better opportunity and rewards? I've lived and worked in our State of Mediocrity all my life so I have nothing to lose by seeing the alternative.'

'Humph! *If* this place exists!' retorted Fixed-Thinking. 'Just because you're still all fired up from that training course you went on last week you're not seeing things the way they really are. But *don't* worry, you'll soon get back to normal, everyone always does. So, go on, off you go. I have no doubt that I'll see you later.'

'Well,' said Indecisive turning back to Smith, 'I'm with *you*, for the moment. Where do we go from here?'

'We must go directly to the Change Border,' answered Smith. 'There we are to gain a pass from Evaluate.'

'Sounds great,' said Indecisive excitedly, 'I want to know more of Prosperity and how soon you think we'll get there. But hey, I'm thirsty. Look let's take a break over there.' Indecisive pointed at the large corner building, full of people eating and drinking. 'I know that place well, it's Procrastination! I have heard that you can enjoy yourself there for as long as you want, do you know it?'

'But I told you that Intuition advised to go directly to Change Border.'

'Oh, come on, we deserve a quick break, don't we?' We'll be able to get on quicker after some refreshment, don't you agree.' Indecisive pushed open the door. 'Hey there's a spare table, quick grab it before someone else beats us to it. Will you get the drinks or shall I?'

◻   ◻   ◻

'WE'RE IN LUCK,' SAID INDECISIVE joining him with a couple of drinks. 'They'd just stopped serving food, but I managed to persuade them to get us something. I wasn't sure what you'd want, so I left it to them to give us whatever was easiest.'

'Lucky,' snapped Smith, 'but this is an *eating* establishment and it's still lunchtime. Do you mean we can't even choose what we want?'

'Well, I spoke to Barman and he said they're short staffed today. He was actually hoping to finish early today himself, as he had such a late night last night. Anyway, if we don't mind waiting he'll try and do what he can.'

Smith looked at the drink stains on the table. He felt annoyed that he had not noticed the mess immediately as his jacket elbow was now stained as well. Given the choice, he liked to eat and drink off a clean table. He noticed a raised area that was cordoned off. It looked slightly more inviting.

'I asked about that when I first came in,' said Indecisive, anticipating Smith. 'Apparently they keep it free in case a large party unexpectedly arrive.'

Smith's thoughts shot to a previous weekend when he had taken his children to a fast food restaurant. An area there had also been cordoned off in preparation for a child's birthday party.

The counter where he had been queuing had been closed upon the arrival of the party guests as the assistant manager, serving his queue, had to leave to cater for their order.

His waiting time was prolonged because he was told to swap to another assistant. This turned out to be a trainee who was uncertain of his till and was constantly pushed aside by colleagues in their rush to prepare their own orders.

'Fries will take a few minutes,' Smith heard as he watched the existing mound being whisked away to fulfil the ravenous party's order. 'Normally we'd bring them to your table, but just come back and shout.'

When Smith commented that perhaps it would be better to wait the assistant had looked at him as if he was an alien. Customers were not meant to confuse staff by making comments. They should only reply to specific questions that would satisfy the demands of the cash registers buttons.

When fully 'trayed-up' for eating in, Smith looked for his children who had gone to find a seat. He spotted them in a corner sitting by a table that was covered in used cartons. Smith noticed that another assistant with a cloth was busily talking to someone that was clearly a friend at another table.

'We would have tidied up ourselves,' said his children, 'but we didn't want to lose our seat. It took us ages to get this one.'

After their meal Smith took his tray of empties towards one of the disposal bins provided. He had been surprised though, during his meal, at how many people just vacated their seats without clearing away. If the majority of us are not even prepared to serve ourselves, thought Smith, what hope is there for giving service to others, let alone expecting it?

'It's busy in here today,' Smith had said to the table-clearing assistant, as he deposited his tray's rubbish.

'Tell me about it,' came the reply, 'and no one clears up after themselves. How they expect me to do it all I don't know.'

'Perhaps they think you're there to do it,' suggested Smith.

Again Smith was looked at as if he was from another planet. 'No, my job is to clean the tables, not *clear* them, that's the customer's job. But because I'm always doing their job, I never have time to do mine.'

Smith had left the restaurant wondering why he had paid a surcharge to eat in. Would he have had to return and shout for his 'fries' if it had been a take out?

'There's nothing we can do other than wait,' said Indecisive, bringing Smith back from his reverie. 'We may as well since we've ordered. Let's have another drink in the meantime - your round I believe.'

'Perhaps it may help if we shout,' said Smith, getting up from his seat.

Having eventually caught the barman's attention, though he continued chatting to another barman while serving, Smith was able to request a cloth and enquire about their food.

'Food orders have finished today, we're short staffed.'

'Yes, I understand that,' said Smith, 'but I believe that someone is preparing something?'

'Not that I know of. Who did you speak to?'

'It was my colleague who ordered, apparently he paid at the same time.'

'Well, I can't help you 'till I know who you spoke to, because they shouldn't have taken your order.' And turning to his fellow barman said, 'did you take an order for *something*?'

'Food orders have finished today, we're short staffed.'

'Yes, I've told him that, but he's already paid.'

'What did he order?'

'Fries?' volunteered Smith, his recent experience fresh in his mind.

'Oh,' said the second barman, 'I noticed a bowl of fries on the counter.'

'Well, perhaps they're ours, though I didn't hear anyone shout'.

'Well,' said the first barman, as if in imitation of Smith, 'don't look at me, it's not my fault.'

Smith took the now cold food and warm drinks back to the table where Indecisive was talking to a person who had joined the table.

'Ah, here you are,' said Indecisive, immediately putting a couple of fries in his mouth. 'Let me introduce you to Complacent. Apparently he's a regular here and has *never* heard of Change Border.' Not seeming to notice the temperature of the food he added, 'and Complacent doesn't think we're on the right road at all.'

'Not at all,' put in Complacent. 'I've lived in this State all my life and been coming here for as long as I can remember and no one has ever asked me where such a place is.'

'Perhaps Fixed-Thinking had a point,' commented Indecisive. 'He told us that we were dreaming.'

'Ah, dreams,' said Complacent, 'I've spoken to many people passing through here about their *dreams*. Fortunately I have been able to put them right about such illusions. Would you believe that someone shared with me her idea of living in Prosperity! I told her, in no uncertain terms, that to live in there could *only* happen if you were born into it, if you had the right education, some special talent or knew people in the right places.'

Indecisive looked accusingly at Smith, 'But I thought anyone could just enter Prosperity?'

'Well, my advice is to not get your hopes up,' continued Complacent, 'and certainly take the time to think about whether you're doing the right thing. Just think of the hassle ahead of you! Have another drink and relax. After all, if it really exists, and I'm not saying it does, it will still be there tomorrow.'

'How could you have led me astray?' said Indecisive, while Complacent went to refill their glasses. 'Surely you're not expecting me to continue now that your mission is a mad idea? We ought to have made certain about where we were going before we gave up what we had. I might have lost everything following you.'

'But I *am* certain,' said Smith surprised at how doubtful he sounded to himself. 'I should not have allowed you to distract me.'

'You should be thanking me instead of blaming me,' retorted Indecisive. 'If it wasn't for me we would be completely lost by now! At least we've found out *your* error before it is too late!' Pausing he saw that Complacent had not bothered to return as he had said he would. He had joined another table where Indecisive was certain that he was talking about the stupidity of the strangers he had just met. They certainly all seemed very amused.

Indecisive imagined how everyone would laugh at him when he returned from following Smith. He would tell them that he had done so only to learn more of Smith ridiculous ideas for a laugh.

They would not believe him at first, he thought, until he had derided Smith. 'I was stupid to listen to you and not Fixed-Thinking,' he continued. 'This is not going to do me any good at all, you and your *Service City*. There's no such place and, as far as *I'm* concerned, there is no need for it anyway. I'm going back and if you had any sense you would too.'

□   □   □

LEFT ALONE AND WITH ONE DRINK following another Smith became disoriented. He swayed from thinking what a fool he was for sharing his intentions with acquaintances, to an immense frustration at being stuck in the rut that he was.

The longer he stayed the harder it was to get started again. Perhaps it was the lack of food against the amount of drink, but the sense of futility for his mission weighed him down. Lacking motivation it took his last remaining will power to force himself to leave Procrastination. In his melancholic state he felt himself falling.

'You look as if you've had a little too much,' consoled Support as she guided Smith out of the sluggish atmosphere. 'A bit of fresh air is what you need.'

'Thank you,' said Smith. 'You're right, it was difficult to breathe in there.'

'Certain atmospheres are as harmful as drugs, and, just as addicted,' replied Support. 'I am not from this State but have heard of this infamous place. Many dreams dissolve into nothing from too long an exposure to Procrastination. Like any addiction, people seem unable to stop themselves from returning here.'

'How can such a place continue to exist?' asked Smith, beginning to feel revived. Sharing his ideas with Fixed-Thinking, Indecisive and Complacent and being almost stuck in Procrastination had taken its toll. He felt vulnerable.

'Because we become comfortable with average and anyone suggesting higher aspirations is frowned upon as being difficult,' answered Support.

Smith thought of the resentment of some of his colleagues when he had been promoted. "I'm better qualified than him," or "I've been here longer" were just some of the stories he had heard from the office cubicles he had vacated. "Better not be seen talking to you now," one had joked, "people will think I'm sucking up." And now, with his ideas on improving service, he knew that many thought "he's only been in the business for five minutes and he thinks he knows better than us already – who does he think he is?"

'I am determined to seek out a better-than-excellent service,' declared Smith, 'yet everyone seems intent on talking the idea down. No one ever wants to see the merits of the possibilities it would bring.'

'People will not see something you want them to, until they are ready, even if what you offer is in their interests,' said Support. 'Why, I even tried to assist someone else in a similar situation to yours recently, and he turned on me for trying to help. It was as if he liked the idea of seeking something different, but lacked any initial fortitude to make a start. Procrastination got to him more than he realised. He's probably still in there with all his dreams put on hold.' With that, Support said good-bye and Smith continued on his way.

❑   ❑   ❑

SMITH HAD NOT GONE FAR WHEN, approaching a crossroads, he noticed a well-dressed gentleman. Now, unknown to the aspiring agent at this time, news of what he was doing had travelled very fast around the State of Mediocrity, as all news about someone doing something out of the ordinary frequently does. This gentleman was Egotist from the town of Mercenary-Policy and he had some specific advice to offer. After initial pleasantries, Egotist asked, 'How far do you have to go?'

'As far as is necessary,' replied Smith.

'And where might that be?' enquired Egotist further.

'Towards Prosperity, via Change Border,' answered Smith.

'My goodness,' said Egotist, 'that's a long way and fraught with obstacles, or so I have heard, for few who have travelled there have ever returned to our State. Why don't you find an easier route? And what of your family? They must be very concerned about this journey that you have embarked upon?'

'They are, but there can be no other alternative for me to follow.'

'But how did you learn of your route, for it is not the best,' said Egotist.

'From Intuition.'

'Ah I thought that might be the case! I am Egotist and I have heard of Intuition but what I have heard is not good at all. He has directed you the most challenging route possible. If you are really in earnest, then you will not be successful by following his counsel. I can see from the stains on the arm of your jacket that you have already fallen into Procrastination. That is just the first of *countless* difficulties that Intuition's road will lead you into.

'Listen to me, for I am much older than you are and have seen much more of the world. It is better to concentrate on getting on with your life. This road to your left leads to the Village of Instant Gratification, where you can visit Conformist Court. Make your way there now and ask to meet with High-Regard. Tell him that I sent you and this honest man will help you, in the same way he has eased many others of their frustration. And, when he has, if you still do not feel like returning back to where you lived, there are vacant apartments, which offer everything that you and your family could want.'

Standing at the crossroads Smith wondered whether it would be wise to follow this gentleman's advice. 'How far is it to Conformist Court?' he asked, 'and which way is the quickest?'

'You're not far at all,' replied Egotist. 'Simply follow this road up over that hill and you'll come straight to the village. You can't miss High-Regard's block, as it is the first one you come to.'

So, Smith turned at the crossroads and made his way up the hill towards the Village of Instant-Gratification. Soon, after reaching the top, the road split into two. How strange, thought Smith, they're absolutely identical. A little confused, as this did not entirely match Egotist's directions, he took the first road, only to come upon another fork with two further identical roads. Again he continued and the same thing happened again. 'But I can't have gone wrong,' thought Smith.

He continued and reached another fork, again with identical roads. 'This is ridiculous,' said Smith out-loud. He retraced his steps but soon came to another fork. 'How can every road be exactly the same as all the others? Where am I?' There were so many now that it seemed to him in his rising panic that the roads were taking him anywhere rather than leading him somewhere. Smith now started to walk faster, as a person does when feeling lost, in an effort to get out of where they are as quickly as they can. 'Why did I listen to that Egotist?' In his increasing panic Smith ran right into Intuition.

'What are you doing here?' enquired Intuition. 'This is the Wilderness of Conformity. A place where countless people have wasted the *whole* of their lives.'

'I was looking for High Regard at Conformist Court,' retorted Smith.

'Yet I directed you towards Change Border,' said Intuition. 'Why have you left the path that you were at first so willing to proceed along?'

'I got stuck in Procrastination. Then, I met a well-dressed gentleman who said he knew an easier path.'

'Sounds like Egotist,' sighed Intuition. 'He and High-Regard both get their fulfilment from appearing better than everyone else. Both are concerned with their position in society, their credibility and the esteem that others hold them in. They seek constant external attractions that in effect only serve to distract them, and the people they influence. Being from the Town of Mercenary-Policy, Egotist works only for the sake of himself, never for the sake of others. He regularly visits the Village of Instant-Gratification because he requires stimulus for his security.

'High-Regard offers to ease frustration with superficial titles, which are meaningless in reality. Any ease is short-lived and soon returns with a weightier vengeance. Once someone has followed their advice they can then only reside in Conformist Court where the company is conducive to not feeling out of place.'

'What an idiot,' confessed Smith. 'To be so easily persuaded off my path is a poor sign of my commitment.'

'Commitment is not something you can manufacture,' consoled Intuition. 'It is what you discover deep down inside of you when you align what you do with what you are. Commitment must be tested for it to grow. Your level of commitment will be as a measure of the strength of your motives for what you do.'

'Now,' continued Intuition, 'continue straight ahead of you and this time keep going until you get there. Follow your heart, and beware distractions. Although tempting, these distractions cannot directly block your road. All they can do is distract you onto theirs. Leaving the road is always your choice.'

1. In work you *produce* something; with
    service you *become* someone.

2. Put your own house before criticising the street.

3. The best way to serve *yourself* is by
    serving *others*.

4. Keep to yourself what is really
    important to you.

5. Beware complacency and fixed thinking.

6. Be Decisive about the choices you want
    make in Life.

7. Profit is applause for the Acts of Service
    performed.

002

Training at Accountability Base

STICKING CLOSELY TO INTUITION'S GUIDANCE this time, Smith arrived at Change Border. The barrier was closed. Smith knocked once, then twice. On the third occasion Evaluate appeared.

'Welcome to Change Border,' said Evaluate looking directly at Smith. So piercing was the gaze that Smith was momentarily lost for words. Never before had he experienced such an appraisal. 'Thank you,' Smith eventually replied. 'Why are you here,' asked Evaluate, 'at this time and alone?'

'I was directed to come here by Intuition,' began Smith. 'And you are right, I had hoped to have been here earlier, and was initially accompanied by some colleagues. But here I am now, alone.'

'Exactly as expected,' said Evaluate. 'When we follow our chosen path, everything happens to us at the right time, and in the right place. So, I take it that you have chosen to leave this State of Mediocrity behind you of your own free will?' said Evaluate.

'Absolutely,' answered Smith.

'How did you assess your colleagues that chose not to go with you?'

'It was clear to me that one was narrow minded and only heard what he wanted to hear,' said Smith. 'The other lacked fortitude and was prone to let others decide for him and then complain when they did so.'

27

'Did you meet with anyone while coming here and, if so, how did you assess them?' enquired Evaluate.

'Yes, I met with Complacent who seemed to be content to procrastinate, almost without conscience,' answered Smith, 'and at a crossroads I met with Egotist, who was only out for himself.'

'From your answers it would appear that you are able to recognise the motives of others quite easily,' said Evaluate. 'Am I to understand, therefore, that you did not allow any of them to influence your own actions? Not *even* the likes of Egotist, whose persuasive reputation goes before him?'

Smith felt like an open book under the unfailing gaze. 'Well not exactly,' he began. 'I suppose in some way they all influenced me to some extent, particularly Egotist, but he seemed so understanding of my situation.'

'And did his freely given advice prove valuable?'

'Not at all, said Smith. 'And if it wasn't for Intuition guiding me back on the right path, I would have been lost in the Wilderness of Conformity.'

'Tell me,' asked Evaluate, 'does the nature of your work require you to assess colleagues, customers, and generally everyone you meet, on a daily basis?'

'Well yes, of course.' replied Smith.

'So you therefore assess *yourself* on a daily basis?'

'I'm not certain what you mean. Assess myself for what?'

'For your own motives of course,' replied Evaluate. 'It is not possible to assess the motives of another, until first you are able to recognise your own. *Do* you consciously evaluate yourself with regard to your own motives daily?'

Smith felt uncomfortable, 'No,' he answered truthfully.

'Have you *ever* evaluated yourself with the serious intention of knowing your motives, values and personal ethos?

'No, I don't believe so,' said Smith quietly.

'Don't be concerned,' consoled Evaluate. 'People habitually evaluate *others*, yet rarely evaluate themselves with the same criteria.'

'When you gain insight into your own actions,' continued Evaluate, 'the behaviour of others becomes clear. There is little point in ensuring that you make all the right moves, when you are unsure of your motives. Yet, when you *are* sure of your motives then the right moves follow.

'That is why, for example, people are generally reluctant to serve others. In assessing another's motives, while unaware of our own, we are in danger of making the wrong moves. Serving another is, therefore, perceived as being servile.'

Evaluate paused as if remembering something, 'Aversion was like that. I remember his clear unwillingness to personally offer service to his customers. He felt that dealing directly with them was beneath him, but wanted his sales people to learn how to do so. Yet we cannot expect others to follow our leadership if we are not prepared to learn and behave in the way that we expect them to perform.

'The assessments you gave me of your colleagues and the people you met on the road, were based on what transpired to you *after* you had allowed yourself to be influenced by them. In recognising their motives *beforehand,* you would have been immune to their adverse influence.'

'But I believe my motives are worthy, so why couldn't I therefore recognise *their* motives?' asked Smith.

'Because we perceive others' motives as we perceive our own to be,' said Evaluate. 'Your motives may indeed be good enough, but it is not until we evaluate them that we become absolutely certain of them. Thus your colleagues mistakenly perceive your motives as similar to theirs, and therefore, possibly ulterior. In turn you assume your colleagues' motives, even Egotist's, to be similar to your own. Tell me, are you able to articulate your motives right here and now for me?'

'Well,' replied Smith, 'I *feel* them more than I can verbalise them. I can tell you that everyday I'm becoming more frustrated with the level of service and lack of care I see around me. I believe that I have to do something positive to change things but I am not certain how to fulfil my potential to do so. Yet I assure you I am willing to learn.'

'Good!' said Evaluate lifting the barrier that separated them. 'Your willingness to escape your State of Mediocrity is clear to me, and, together with your determination, such willingness gains you passage. Here, come through and I will direct you on the next step of your journey.'

Evaluate handed Smith a piece of paper and pointed at the road directly in front of him. 'The way ahead of you is known as The Road of Assessment. You must stay on the road until you came to Accountability Base. Upon your arrival present this evaluation sheet. Accountability will then prepare you further for your journey to Prosperity.'

❑   ❑   ❑

SMITH FELT GOOD AS HE WALKED DOWN The Road of Assessment. He was still aware of his frustration, though the firm action he was now taking was alleviating it.

Perhaps it was his imagination, yet it seemed the air was different. He could breathe deeper than before and could think more clearly. 'This is a strange road,' he said to himself, 'it's not like any other I have been down before. I feel like asking myself questions that I have never asked before, yet in the sure knowledge that the answer will be immediately forthcoming.'

He unrolled the sheet of paper and began to read the questions.

'Why do you continue to do only what others think is best for you?'

Well that's easy he thought, 'Because I lack belief in myself.'

Next question:

'Why do you feel different when talking to someone you want something from, than when you are talking to someone that you do not want something from?'

'Because I lack self-confidence.'

'Why do you use a fraction of your potential?' asked another.

'Because I am unaware of my true power,' was his answer.

'Why do act as your own worst enemy?'

'Because I don't really like myself.'

'Why are you so easily put off from your course?'

'Because I lack the courage of my convictions.'

'Why do you exist?

'To fulfil my purpose.'

'What is your purpose?'

'To fulfil my potential.'

◻   ◻   ◻

SMITH LOOKED UP FROM THE COMPLETED evaluation sheet, and saw before him a long building set back from the road within a walled courtyard. 'This must be Accountability Base,' he said to himself.

Without pausing, Smith crossed the elegant courtyard, walked up to the large entrance door and rang the bell. The door was opened.

'So you have a completed evaluation sheet for me to consider,' said Accountability expectantly.

'I do indeed,' replied Smith.

'Good, it is not until we crystallise our thoughts that we confirm how we really feel about something, particularly our destiny.'

'In important matters of your destiny, there are three of you. As you truly are; you as you think you are; and you as you want others to think that you are. Too often we become so used to relying on others advice that we cease to trust in ourselves. With personal assessment we receive the right answers. Answers that are infinitely more meaningful than those we simply just want to hear.'

'Now, come on in. I'll show you to your room first and later you will meet the others, all of whom are heading towards Prosperity.'

'Is it a long way?' enquired Smith.

'Longer for some than others,' replied Accountability, 'which is why your preparation is so important. See you downstairs in the Library.'

After refreshing himself, Smith made his way downstairs.

'It's a beautiful day,' said Enthusiasm.

'How long have you been here?' Asked Smith.

'This is my third and last day,' came the reply, 'and the time has absolutely raced by. It always does of course when you're enjoying yourself.'

'I've only just arrived,' said Smith, 'I hope I didn't miss anything.'

'I wouldn't give it another thought,' said Enthusiasm. 'Accountability says that it is not possible to miss the important lessons of life. And, as we only learn from them when we are ready to receive them, there is little advantage in trying to rush them is there?'

Enthusiasm's light-hearted positive attitude was infectious and Smith soon found himself laughing as they made their way to the Library together.

'I see that you have met with Enthusiasm,' began Accountability. 'No doubt he will have told you that he is leaving us today to continue on his mission. You can learn from him, so take the opportunity to talk with him before he departs.

'Here are Experience and Youth,' he continued while looking at the two with fond amusement. 'They travel together, though I believe most of their time is spent in disagreement.'

'It's only because he refuses to listen to me,' they said in unison while pointing at each other.

'It's always the same when they are together,' said Accountability, while guiding Smith across the room, 'both of them continually know what to do for the best. Together, however, they make up a strong team, though do not yet realise it. One is more patient than the other, and one is more passionate. Both virtues are complementary.

'Now, here we have Redundant and Anxious, who arrived by different roads. And lastly, though by no means least, this is Persistence and Discipline, former students and now colleagues, who drop in from time to time.'

Smith turned to Accountability: 'Different roads? I thought there was only one way to Service City, and that was via Change Border?'

'That's the perfect question with which to commence,' he replied and turning to address everyone said: 'Prosperity occupies its own State of Mind – a state brought about by a change in our thinking. Yet we must not seek change for change's sake, but for our own sake, to fulfil our potential. Different roads lead to different Change Borders. Boundaries each must pass through in our own way.'

'By addressing questions that we alone can only answer?' asked Smith.

'Partly,' replied Accountability. 'The Road of Assessment is certainly effective when frustration is involved. Redundant here required another route.'

'Yes,' said Redundant, 'For me it was the Road of Dilemma that changed my thinking. And it was not until I walked it that I was able to see how my predicament would benefit me. I met with Opportunity, who had been passing me by, but then turned and chose to travel with me and brought me here. Opportunity asked questions of me, which prompted me to consider the future differently. That's when I met with Enthusiasm, who brought me to Accountability.

'The important thing is that the roads we choose lead us to taking ownership for decisions and responsibility for our actions,' said Accountability.

'That sounds all well and good but what if it's just not possible to be on the right road, let alone answer any questions?' asked Anxious.

'By which route did you come to be here then?' enquired Smith.

'Evaluate put me on the Road of Apprehension, then told me I could leave it whenever I wanted. I said it was easy for him to say that, but what if I did and then got lost? But, as I was looking at the road before me, he disappeared just leaving me with a blank sheet of paper.'

'Did any questions and answers come to you?' asked Smith.

'Well, in fact, one question did spring to mind,' answered Anxious. 'It was *why are you so fearful about things that never happen?*'

'And did an answer come to you?' said Smith.

'Well, not really. It was more like a series of alternatives though the clearest answer was: Because I enjoy being so.

'Anyway,' continued Anxious, 'just after reading that I met with Self-Pity, who feeling sorry for me, said he knew somewhere where I might find help, and brought me to the back door of this place. The back door I tell you, just the sort of thing that happens to me!'

'You know that you could have quite easily come around to the front entrance,' said Accountability. 'I believe you already knew that, didn't you?'

'I suppose I did,' Anxious replied, 'and did think about it but on second thoughts, thought better of it. I hope you weren't offended,' he added worriedly.

'Perhaps it would be better to have second thoughts first then,' replied Accountability. 'Though do not concern yourself, for here the front and back doors are one and the same. There can only be one way to enter into taking personal responsibility, which is why you are all here. In preparing yourself to fulfil your mission, there is one prime directive. That is: irrespective of your choices in life, you must always take responsibility for *whatever* happens to you, and always take ownership of that which is important to you, or have promised yourself, or another, to follow through.'

'But what if you choose to not do anything?' said Youth.

'As even non-choice is a choice by default, you must learn that there is always a choice,' answered

Accountability. 'The world recognises no neutral. There is only moving forward or falling back. Our choices or non-choices generate our progress or lack of it.'

'Surely you don't mean that if I choose not to do anything, I regress?' asked Experience. 'What if such a decision is appropriate? I have learned that it is often wiser to do nothing, rather than something in a particular situation.'

'Do not mistake non-choice for wrong choice,' replied Accountability.' When correct, non-choice will propel you forward, as an incorrect actual choice will force you back. As our choices ultimately shape our destiny, and certainly the level of our success, it is important to learn how to choose correctly.'

'But how is it possible to do that?' said Anxious.

'By choosing to establish what is important to us, how we want to live, what we want to do and why we do. Then ensure that our future choices follow this established format. Success, for example, is based on good judgement that in turn is based on experience. And from where is experience gained?'

'Bad judgement,' said Youth, while poking Experience in the ribs.

'Correct,' said Accountability, 'as I am sure your colleague agrees.'

'It would be wrong of me to say otherwise,' said Experience. 'For I have gained more experience through having to handle my mistakes, than anything else. And certainly the choices I either make, or choose not to make, these days are infinitely better than they were years ago, though I cannot admit to them being within an established framework. But then that is why I am here.'

'By which road then did get here?' asked Smith.

'By the Road of Futility,' replied Experience, 'where I learned that a wealth of knowledge is useless without purposeful goals to harness and direct it.'

'That was my road too, though my questions were not the same as yours, were they?' said Youth looking at Experience. 'I discovered that unless I take the time to know what I really want to do in my life, I would never fulfil my potential.'

'Certainly, you must enjoy, even love what you do in life to make the most of your potential,' cut in Enthusiasm.

'Let's get real here,' said Anxious. 'You can't always do what you *enjoy* doing. Sometimes, in fact most of the time, I don't enjoy what I do, but I do it because I have to. How else could I afford to live.'

'When people choose, usually through non-choice, to *not* do what they really want, they will complain about what they *have* to do, even though they do not know what they would *rather* do,' said Accountability. 'If only they could stop to think about what they truly enjoy doing and work towards it.'

'Often people take more time trying to get out of something, than just getting on with it,' said Discipline. 'If they were to put some energy and enthusiasm into the task, they would get more out of it and so would their customer.'

'Yes!' exclaimed Smith. 'I'm sure that's exactly what happens when people serve others. Sometimes when you walk up to a service counter, people seem determined to make you wait before even acknowledging you. It's as if they are doing you a huge favour when they finally do.'

'It's certainly a good feeling being acknowledged.' said Enthusiasm. 'It's about feeling valued.'

☐　　　　☐　　　　☐

'WHENEVER PEOPLE ARE UNCERTAIN ABOUT what they really want to do, they feel insecure,' said Accountability. 'Whenever people harbour insecurities, whatever they are and for whatever reason, they will compensate by seeking control over others. Controlling another, even just keeping them waiting, restores a sense of power within an individual. Though, in reality, this power is short-lived as it is a false sense of security.

'To serve another well,' Accountability continued, 'is therefore perceived as a weakness, instead of the strength that it really is. I said earlier that Prosperity was a State of Mind that required a different level of thinking. A level that recognises that giving service is a strength; that understands the importance of continuous personal and professional development, in order to fulfil potential; and that acknowledges the importance of aligning what we do, with what we are, within a specific framework of mission, values and goals.

'The future of worthwhile success is exemplified in Service City. Those of you who are on a mission to reach there will discover that actions speak louder than words. On the road there, however, you will encounter many places where words are valued over actions. Some use words so much that they end up resting solely on them for future growth and relying on them for establishing a reputation or position in the marketplace.

'Every day I work with people that focus on what they can say to market products in the most exciting way,' agreed Smith. 'The meaning is lost in the method. Their aim is merely to move products as quickly as possible and the fact that what they are saying about these products may be untrue seems of little interest to them. It's all part of the job as far as they are concerned!'

'On the road here you all questioned your motives for the mission you are undertaking. Because you now understand what they are you must make your own decisions based on those motives. We have shared with each other the importance of recognising our power of choice. Always remember that, irrespective of your circumstances and conditions, you are where you are *because* of your previous choices or non-choices.

'It follows, therefore, that you can become what you want to be, do what you want to do and have what you want to have, when you make a definite choice to take action. This action involves accepting full personal responsibility for whatever happens in your life. However hard it is for you to accept this, it is vital that you still do so. You, and only you, are responsible for you.'

❑   ❑   ❑

'FOLLOWING THIS TRUTH, YOU MUST ALWAYS choose to take ownership of your decisions and become accountable for following them through,' Accountability turned towards Discipline and Persistence: 'Tell us of the roads that brought you here?'

'I have always chosen the same road whenever I visit here,' began Discipline. 'I know it well and the more that I continue to travel it, the faster I seem able to move. Straight, though well worn, as it is often used for exercise, it is named the Road of Preparation.'

'It sounds a good road,' said Smith, 'but do the same questions come to you each time you walk it?'

'They are similar yet seem to become more testing each time,' replied Discipline, 'and though the answers differ slightly, they become more accurate each time. I remember one of the first questions was *Why do you keep putting things off?* To which my answer came: Because they are not important.

39

'Then, another time it was: *Why do you keep putting important things off?* This time my answer was: Because they are important. A third time I thought, *Why do you leave what is so important for you to do until the last minute?* And my answer was: Because I am lazy.'

'Surely that can't be right,' said Smith. 'You appear to be so, well, *orderly*, if you understand me.'

'Thank you, but I wasn't always,' replied Discipline. 'Travelling the Road of Preparation taught me that laziness comes when we lack motivation for what we want to achieve. Having a goal is not as important as the knowing *why* you want to achieve it. When you have many reasons for *why* you actually want to be, do or have something, the *preparation* important to ensure their fulfilment becomes something you look forward to.'

'I agree,' said Persistence. 'It is the lack of *reasons* that many people fail to achieve their goals. Travelling the Road of Tenacity, as I did, taught me the importance of measuring the belief in oneself. A belief that can only be really proved when it becomes clear that you will stick to doing something regardless of the obstacles that are in the way of its achievement.'

'That may be true, but most people lack goals, let alone reasons to have them,' said Anxious.

'We must always have goals, because if we don't know where we are going, how will we recognise it when we get there?' replied Persistence. 'That is why we feel lost even when in familiar surroundings. The difficulty is that people generally only have goals for what they want to have.'

'And you cannot have before you do, nor do before you can become what you have decide that you really want to be,' said Discipline.

'Absolutely, and you can only be tenacious in following through your goals, if they excite you,' added Persistence.

'Excitement is the measure of how much you want to achieve them,' added Enthusiasm.

'Where I used to work, we were told to make goals, but to be honest none of them really *excited* me,' said Redundant.

'That's because they had no meaning to you,' said Accountability. 'And the danger is that when we have no belief in what we are doing, it is reflected in our attitude and behaviour towards others. You might say that we become *de-meaning* towards others.'

'I suppose I did feel a little like that, but I did enjoy my work. It's what I knew and I was good at it. Though there was very little praise from anyone,' said Redundant. 'I was part of a strategy team for my former employer, All Tech-no-Com. Our team's role was to formulate innovative ways to get our customers to stay with us, rather than leave and join one of our many competitors. This was quite challenging because in our industry a product could be out of date almost as soon as it was available.

'Unless we were able to create a particular strategy and get it adopted quickly and prove that it was generating growth, it would lose its impetus and our work would be in vain. Because of this, not as much preparation was carried out as perhaps should have been. And seldom were we able to follow things through because someone in another department would veto it. Would you believe that as many as five signatures from various senior managers were required before something could be agreed to? Anyway, and to make matters worse, one of the signatories, would ratify strategy only on the basis of how it affected him. His name was Credit-Seek and I am sure that he was responsible for many colleagues and myself being considered as an unnecessary overhead.'

'He was responsible?' said Accountability. 'Remember that regardless of whatever happens we must take responsibility.'

'But why should I,' protested Redundant, 'if it wasn't my fault?'

'When you take responsibility for whatever happens you let go of the emotional baggage the experience has created,' answered Accountability. 'Blaming others looks backward; whereas solution seeking, derived from taking responsibility, looks only forward. *And* you have recently learned that when you look forward, opportunity appears.'

'It does seem that the higher some people go in a company the more they become concerned about securing what they have already achieved,' said Smith. 'It's almost as if their focus changes from aspiring to what they want, to one of keeping what they have achieved.'

'Well, Credit-Seek, was certainly one of those,' said Redundant. 'He used all the experience that he had gained over the years to recognise what would bring benefit to him.'

'That must have been demoralising for your team,' said Smith.

'It certainly was. Mind you, the service team had a worse deal. As All Tech-no-Com insisted on zero defects as a policy they set up a specific rapid response Service Team to ensure that this could be brought about. Their job was to use their technology to know about an occurring fault even *before* the customer. They were so successful that they were never mentioned, until Finance saw what they were spending and immediately reduced their budget. Shortly afterwards Service Team were taken to task for allowing defects and customer complaints to increase.'

'But your company must have recognised that Service Team's budget had been solely responsible for reduced customer complaints?' asked Smith.

'Not really,' replied Redundant, 'for now they had invested in a customer complaints department they needed to justify its existence. Finance decided that it was pointless having two expensive units, so one of them had to be cut. Service Team was axed.'

◻   ◻   ◻

DURING THE COURSE OF THE NEXT THREE DAYS, Smith spent time with each of Accountability's guests. 'I don't see how anything can be achieved without your involvement,' he said to Enthusiasm, prior to the latter's departure on the first day. 'Couldn't you stay just a little longer, for there is so much more I want to ask you?'

'You'll be fine,' Enthusiasm replied. 'The rate at which you are working on yourself it will not be long before you run into your own inspiration. And, it is a far better thing to acquire your own strength, than simply borrow strength from another. For in doing the latter, that which we have the ability to do well and really excel at, can be lost to us.'

'But how can we be sure that we have such strength and abilities?' Smith asked. 'Surely some people are simply more gifted than others are? After all, we can't all be geniuses.'

'Why not?' answered Enthusiasm. 'Of course we can, because we already are. It's simply that the majority of people have been conditioned to believe that they are ordinary, instead of the *extra*ordinary beings that they really are. Those that are able to express the real extraordinary self are simply acting in harmony with their true potential. Others that are so occupied with what they think they should be *doing* never find the time to follow their heart's desire for *being* what they are capable of becoming. The determining factor is how strong the desire is. For though many desires may be ignited almost all are allowed to fizzle out.'

'But it's not good to always desire something is it?' asked Smith.

'Why ever not? It's the most natural emotion in the world. The desire to survive is shared by every living creature. The desire to grow and fulfil its potential is the very element of Nature itself. Does a tree grow to half its height? No, it grows as tall as it possibly can. Desire is a positive and vital part of being human, though, like many powerful factors, its power can be abused and mistakenly applied.'

'How exactly?' asked Smith, 'I have to admit that whenever I've had the desire to do something that I believe will improve my life, I've always felt guilty for not just being satisfied with what I already have.'

'It isn't good to be *dis*satisfied, but this is not the same as being *un*satisfied,' replied Enthusiasm. 'When you follow your heart, excitement inevitably grows, and, as I discovered for myself on the Road of Devotion, your growing enthusiasm soon rids you of any false guilt.'

'I was wondering by what road you came to be here,' said Smith.

'It was the perfect road for me, as I learned to devote myself to what was important to me,' said Enthusiasm. 'Now my eagerness for what I am doing knows no bounds and the wonderful thing is that the more I share it with others, the more I seem to have.'

'Well, it is certainly contagious,' laughed Smith. 'I can feel it growing in me.'

'And you must allow it to continue to do so as it is the armour that will protect you against adversaries. Now I must go. Goodbye.'

'What adversaries?'

'The ones you seek out yourself, of course,' called out Enthusiasm.

▫   ▫   ▫

'COMING THROUGH THE STATE OF CHAOS on my way here was not easy,' said Discipline, 'but the key is to not quarrel, or fall out, with anyone there. It is to marshal Chaos because when it is organised around a purpose a lot of creativity is forthcoming.'

'How can good come from being in such a State,' said Smith, who had begun his conversation with Discipline by asking where he was from.

'Few people living outside such a State and even those people who choose to live there seldom accept that it is possible. Yet the best disciplines come out of such an environment. Why even out of the chaos of an exploding void came the creation of a Universe that maintains itself in perfect balance.'

'How do you go about marshalling chaos for creativity, and why would the outcome create good attributes of discipline?' enquired Smith.

'I didn't say that one led to the other,' replied Discipline, 'indeed both are independent. Though they may emanate from the same environment conducive for them, they follow different paths. To marshal chaos requires the ability to communicate a unified vision that harnesses the energies of all, for the benefit of all. Irrespective of the vision, receptivity for what it will deliver must be created. When people believe in a vision, the potential that is released because people *want* to work, rather than have to, for a common purpose, is immeasurable. If you are successful in entering Service City you will learn more on this subject, but first you must cultivate certain attributes to be able to get there.'

'I am willing to learn whatever is necessary,' volunteered Smith.

'Good,' said Discipline. 'Because there may be adversaries ahead of you that *must* be fought.'

'Do I *have* to?' asked Smith. 'Surely there must be an alternative.'

'There is, but people rarely find it. It's as if they attract the adversary, whichever way they go. If it meets you, this destroyer of dreams, will viciously attack you. Known as Security-itis, this assassin has defeated many aspiring agents that have sought Prosperity.'

'How can I protect myself?' cried Smith.

'The armour Enthusiasm advised you carry within you will help. Also take one step at a time and don't give way to the assassin's attack.'

'Because for every step you take in the face of adversity, the more belief and confidence grow in you,' added Persistence, who joined the conversation.

'Yes, I remember one agent, Analysis, who was zealous about the path he was taking,' said Discipline. 'His self-control was clear but he lacked the tenacity to follow things through. No sooner would he come upon an obstacle than he would back off and take another path. He was the most organised and prepared of agents, but always preferred to go round in circles.'

'Did he get where he was going in the end, though?' asked Smith.

'Well, the last I heard of him was that he was trying to cross the Chasm of Professional Complacency, just outside Service City.'

'Another agent I remember,' said Persistence, 'excelled at perseverance, yet lacked self-government, so he was never prepared to move forward.'

'That's right,' added Discipline, 'his name was Paralysis. And now the two of them unintentionally cause doubts in the minds of other agents they meet.'

'But together they could have helped each other,' said Smith.

'I'm afraid that's not always the case, especially when both impediments hold the most influence,' answered Discipline. 'The result is that the team of Analysis Paralysis now perceive their duty as one of confronting and questioning aspiring agents to see if they should really continue forward or turn back.'

□   □   □

SHORTLY BEFORE HIS OWN DEPARTURE, Smith went to see Accountability. His host was in conversation with Anxious and Redundant.

'Our self-concept is effectively our command centre,' said Accountability. 'And whatever we believe about ourselves becomes true, as we act in a manner which is consistent with those beliefs. There are three parts to our command; our self-ideal, or the person we would most like to be; our self-image, or the person we think ourselves to be; and our self-esteem, or how much we feel we like the person that we are.'

'I still don't see how learning to like ourselves more puts us on the road to improvement,' said Anxious. 'What will people think of us if they find out we are wanting to like ourselves more?'

47

'Well, as I understand it,' said Redundant, 'if we dislike ourselves 100%, we're can't really believe in ourselves. If self-confidence must be acquired to reach our self-ideal, then I for one am going to learn to like myself more. Mind you, it's going to be hard because I never really valued myself as much as I should have.'

'A person's self-worth receives many knocks,' offered Accountability, 'even by well meaning people. But your self-esteem will grow in direct proportion to how much you like and respect yourself. And you must respect yourself. Indeed your self-respect is the greatest treasure you possess, so you must never give it away by being embarrassed for who you are, or what you do.'

'I have learned during these last few intensive days,' put in Smith, 'that the development of a wholesome self-respect and positive self-image are closely related to the recognition of the potential that exists in each of us.'

'Quite right,' said Accountability, 'and we must never short-circuit our chances of releasing such potential by having a poor self-image. One that insists on us placing a ceiling on all of our genuinely attainable aspirations.'

'Come on,' said Redundant to Anxious, 'let's go and continue our studies on this one. There's no way I want to limit what I want to do and where I want to go, now that I have met with Opportunity!'

Accountability turned towards Smith, 'Well, your stay here is at an end and I am sure that you are eager to continue on your way.'

'I am indeed, ready or not,' answered Smith.

'You are as ready as you will ever be, for it is only through following your destiny that you prepare yourself for it,' said Accountability.

'I am concerned about forthcoming obstacles, though hopefully I won't meet with them,' said Smith. 'But my resolve is firm and I will meet what I must.'

'Experience will tell you that for every battle won or lost, you emerge stronger,' said Accountability. 'If you ask Youth, he will tell you that to live and not to risk, is not to be born. Both are right, as usual of course, and in truth, timber becomes stronger through rough weather. You may feel your resolve is firm, but it will not be until it is tested on the road that you will see if it remains firm.'

'You believe that I will have fight Security-itis, then?'

'I hope not, but it is better that we go into the unknown with as much preparation as we are able to draw upon. Remember to always keep your mind on what you want, why you want it, and why it caused you to escape the State of Mediocrity. Never allow yourself to be persuaded to dwell on what you don't want because you may discover, as many others have done to their downfall, that you unconsciously gravitate toward it.'

'Now,' said Accountability, 'allow me to set you in the right direction, for there is someone else that you must meet. There is no need to leave the way you entered. When we take ownership for what happens to us in our lives, there can be no going back to how we were. In the Courtyard, there is an opening in the side of the wall. Pass through it and follow the sound of water. Near a lake you will see someone who is waiting there to speak to you.'

'But who is it?' enquired Smith with curiosity.

'You'll see,' answered Accountability.

<<< AGENT SMITH FILE NOTE >>>

1. Consciously evaluate your motives regularly.

2. Crystallise your thoughts in writing.

3. Take responsibility for your life and ownership of your dreams.

4. You are where you are because of previous or non-choices.

5. Acquire your strength rather than borrow another's.

6. Self-respect is your greatest treasure never to be buried.

7. Without purposeful goals, knowledge has low value.

8. The ability to communicate vision harnesses all energies.

9. Self-esteem grows when you like and respect yourself.

003

Scaling the Heights of Reluctance

FOLLOWING THE SOUND OF WATER SMITH came upon a stream where the water persistently carved a path through the stony ground. Tracking downstream Smith came to where the waterfall tumbled into a lake. Suddenly the sunlight flashed so brightly off the water that his vision was momentarily impaired.

'Ah,' said Inspiration, 'I've been expecting you. You have just left Accountability Base, was the time you spent there useful?'

'Most definitely,' answered Smith. 'To understand the importance of taking personal responsibility for entering Prosperity.'

'Good, so you have come here to develop your own Charter then?'

'Have I?' replied Smith with uncertainty.

'Yes, because, when you accept the importance of evaluating yourself and taking responsibility for what you do, the time has come to create your own Charter for what you stand for.'

'My own Charter?' repeated Smith.

'Absolutely,' said Inspiration. 'A guiding statement that serves as a reminder to align what you do with what you are. You cannot enter Service City without this identity and it is essential to becoming a Secret Service operative. Good agents know what they *stand* for. They are committed to setting *the* service standard that one day the whole world will aspire to. The Founder there

51

only accepts the very best and wants those people that give their best *because they want to.*'

'Then what must I do to reach this standard?' asked Smith.

'Look at this lake in front of us,' began Inspiration. 'It owes it size, to the small stream that fills it. It is the lake's conduit for life. From the moment it springs from its source the stream has a mission: to realise its purpose. Taking the path of least resistance, it does not force itself; yet overcomes all by its commitment to keep going. It harnesses each obstacle as allies to carve its path, its own statement. This stream carries no frustration; it simply gets on with its mission

'Now, tell me,' continued Inspiration, 'what do you do and is there a mission statement where you work?'

'I am the Customer Service director at Communication Limited in the City of Apathy, the capital of the State of Mediocrity,' replied Smith. 'And yes, we have a mission statement.'

'Was everybody in the company asked to be involved in developing it?'

'No,' answered Smith, 'and many of those that were asked were not really concerned about being involved.'

'Because they considered it as just another programme of the month?' enquired Inspiration.

'Well, yes, I suppose some people have made comments to that effect.'

'And the people who were involved in producing it, did they already have personal mission statements?'

'Not that I know of, because I wasn't involved in it too much either.'

'Would you say that a harmonious atmosphere existed? One that was conducive to a sense of belonging?'

Smith thought of the duplicitous, 'that's-not-your-job' and 'didn't-you-know' environment that was prevalent at Communication Limited. 'I think that developing and communicating the mission to everyone was supposed to create harmony, but it hasn't. Most ignore it and get on with what they have to do. In fact, our company's culture is not good, we're a communication company yet we don't seem able to communicate between ourselves, let alone our customers.'

'A legal document may form a company,' said Inspiration. 'But it is people that make it come alive. And it is how they think and feel about what they do that develops the culture. Commitment is short-lived unless people understand what a mission involves. This can only happen by developing one for themselves first.'

'It does seem to make sense for individuals to have their own mission,' said Smith. 'It's true that the mission of Communication Limited has not been bought into. Few were part of the process, so have little belief in what it stands for. But surely they'd need some guidance otherwise everybody would do their own thing?'

'What's important in developing a personal mission is that in doing so each of us can align what is *important to us* with what we *actually do*. During the process most people accept that they have been resistant to new ideas, not realising that it was actually important to them too. A few may choose to leave, realising they are not giving as much as they should, because their interest lies elsewhere. Such action is good for both company and individual. Some people may work just to pay bills, but who really wants to have a lifetime career doing something they actually do not enjoy or believe in? You could say that: People do not die from hard work; they die from hard work they hate.'

'Well people do seem to do that where I come from,' admitted Smith.

'Which is why they are still in the State of Mediocrity where moaning about work and working to moan go hand in glove,' replied Inspiration emphatically. 'Yet when everyone embarks on a personal mission as part of the process of developing a company mission the end result is everyone shares a unified purpose.

'Clearly, the leaders who are responsible for driving the business and whose prime function is to communicate the vision of where it is going and why, have a duty to provide guidance. But they can only achieve this through example. Above all, they must go through the process of knowing what they stand for. If not, how can it be possible to develop something that reflects what everyone involved in a business stands for? And when people or businesses don't know what they stand for, then they will fall for anything.'

'Intuition told me that it is not possible to complain about the state of the street, unless first your own house is in order,' said Smith.

'And as always, he is right,' said Inspiration. 'And as you have done the groundwork to put your house in order, are you now ready to know what you stand for? To embrace those values and principles that will guide your every decision?'

'Yes,' said Smith, 'though I am not sure how to put my feelings into words.'

'Go for it anyway. Just let the words flow. What gives you your frustration?'

'Not being able to do what I know I am capable of.'

'Which is?'

'Delivering what I fully believe in, selling what I believe in, marketing what I believe in, being what I believe in.'

'Which is?'

'Making a difference in the lives of others and thereby continually improving my own.'

'Following the principle that the best way to learn is to teach?' offered Inspiration.

'Yes, because the best way to serve yourself is to serve others,' said Smith, feeling the words coming from his heart.

'So?'

'I stand for learning about myself through teaching good service.

'I stand for treating everyone equally in the same way that I would like to be treated irrespective of title, rank, background, education, colour, sex, or creed.

'I stand for treating the person *behind* the desk in the same way as the person *in front of* the desk.

'I stand for treating the person in front of the desk as if he, or she, were my customer for life, even if they are not.

'I stand for continually seeking ways to surprise the people that I serve, by going the extra mile.

'I stand for *people* before *products*, *service* before *selling*, and *relationships* before *marketing*.

'I stand for doing the right thing, before doing things right, even if it means *losing* a sale. Because I stand for *delivering* what my customer wants, before *selling* them what I want.

'Above all, I stand for *character* before *personality* and being internally motivated rather than externally influenced.'

Smith paused, took a deep breath and said. '*I stand to deliver.*'

'Excellent!' said Inspiration. 'The simplest statements are always the best to remind us of what we stand for, particularly when doubts cause us to question what we are about.'

'I feel different, lighter, more confident, I am more certain of my direction!' said Smith, excitedly.

'You are now ready to continue your journey towards Prosperity,' said Inspiration. 'Take your Charter for what you stand for, and keep it safe,' said Inspiration. 'Don't lose it, because you will need it to enter Service City. Take the road beyond the lake that leads towards the Heights of Reluctance and you must take the path that leads to the very top. It is by far the best route to the Integrity House where you will be able to rest. Good luck!'

□   □   □

SMITH FOLLOWED THE ROAD BEYOND the lake towards the Heights of Reluctance. As he approached it he saw that the path split into three ways. Two were going around the Hill and one continued upwards. There were two people at the junction.

'Ah,' said Quick-Fix seeing Smith. 'Here's someone who can share his story while we walk, making the time pass quicker.'

'Well, it would be good to wile away a couple of hours,' said Trivia, to his companion and turning towards Smith added, 'Hi, you're just in time to join us.'

'Good,' said Smith amicably, 'I would like that, though this Hill looks steeper than it did at a distance. We might not have enough breath to talk as well eh?'

'You're not considering taking that route are you?' said Quick-Fix. 'Taking this side road will get us to our destination much faster.'

'Well, I'm not sure where you two are heading, but my destination is House Integrity,' said Smith pointing to the road that led up.

'That won't get you anywhere in a hurry,' scoffed Quick-Fix. 'No, this side road is much easier and will still get us there. I've heard of Integrity House, it's on the road to Good Fortune, which is where we're bound for anyway. So, if you come with us, I'm sure that we will pass by the place.'

'Our way is far more enjoyable,' added Trivia. 'There are lots of things to see on the way that are great for occupying the mind while walking and talking.'

'Much as I appreciate your kind offer of company and conversation, I will go my own way,' said Smith. 'Yes, it is steep, but I take the view that I will be rewarded for my efforts.'

'I have to warn you that taking that road will be a bad choice,' argued Quick-Fix. 'We tried it, let me tell you, but the path looked as if it led nowhere.'

'And it was boring, as well as tiring,' added Trivia. 'Come on, join us, the more the merrier I always say.'

'No,' said Smith, surprised at how firm he sounded. 'This path is for me, onwards and up, I say.'

'Well more fool you!' retorted Quick-Fix. 'You don't know *what* you're missing out on,' and turning to his companion added, 'come-on we've wasted enough time as it is. Let's go!'

Smith watched the two as they left. After a couple of minutes Smith saw Trivia stop and beckon to Quick-Fix and then point at something in the distance. A moment later Trivia stopped again and once more beckoned his companion. This happened a couple more times until it appeared to Smith that the two were exchanging heated words. Quick-Fix then turned and walked back to the junction.

'So, you've decided to join me after all,' said Smith.

'There's no way I'm scaling those heights,' replied Quick-Fix breathlessly. 'No, I'm just taking this other side road, which will be just as quick I'm sure. And I'll be much faster than being bogged down with Trivia over there! I can't imagine for one moment how he finds so much time to waste in trying to get where he's going.'

◻   ◻   ◻

'I'M SURE THIS IS GETTING STEEPER,' thought Smith after he had been climbing for what seemed ages. 'This is hard work and I am only about half way up.'

'At least you stopped at the best place to rest, just look at the view.'

'And how do you know that it's the best place?' asked Smith pleasantly.

'Well, I should know it well by now! My name's Habit and this idyllic place is Comfort Zone. Here, come and take a break for a while, you've earned it!'

'Thanks,' said Smith, while introducing himself and choosing a spot to sit down. 'You're right, it seems a good place to rest.'

'And a great view to enjoy as well, eh?' said Habit.

'Then it must be pretty spectacular from the top,' commented Smith. 'What is it like and how much further is it?'

'Haven't the faintest idea,' replied Habit. 'I've never seen the point in going right to the top. And why should I bother? I know this ground well now and it suits me just fine.'

'Well surely it's worth going up sometime or other?' asked Smith.

'I've often thought about it,' answered Habit, 'but each time I do, it always seems to be such an effort to actually do so.'

'Can I ask where you're from and where you are heading then?' said Smith.

'Certainly but first would you like a cup of coffee or something?'

Smith was pleased to be offered a drink, gratefully accepted and settled back into the soft carpet of grass to enjoy it.

'I started out from Familiar Town in the State of Mediocrity,' began Habit.

'That's the same State I started out from,' interrupted Smith.

Looking out at the view before him, Habit seemed to ignore the interruption and continued talking.

'Though *I* actually had no intention of ever leaving, it was my girlfriend, Curious, who persuaded me to do so. She had heard something about Prosperity and wanted to visit. Well, I had got used to being in her company, so her suggestion to go there together seemed like a good idea at the time. It was hard to leave though. I like Familiar and to leave, well it just didn't feel right.'

'So where is Curious now?' asked Smith.

'Well, if you give me a chance, I'll get to that. It's my story you know, so you'll have to let me tell it the way I always do!' replied Habit. 'Anyway,' he continued again, 'we came to this gate'

'Would that be Change Border?' put in Smith.

Habit looked annoyed. '*Anyway*, it may well have been what you say, but as we couldn't find anyone in attendance, Curious decided that we should duck under the barrier and just go through. Well, we did that, which did not rest easy with me at all. However, we found the Road of Inclination, which was a nice road and suited us both and it led straight to these Heights. We decided to take the middle of the three road junction at the bottom, simply because it was the middle one, which is something I have always done and we reached this point.'

Habit paused for some coffee and though Smith wanted to ask something, thought better of interrupting him.

'Anyway, I didn't like coming up this hill but when I reached this place it reminded me of home, so I soon warmed to it. But Curious wouldn't settle. She suggested that as the road ahead was getting steeper she would go back down and check out where the other roads led. So, as we were getting on each other's nerves a bit, I stayed here and she went to investigate. And that's how I came to be here. Lucky old me to find this place, that's what I say. Don't you agree?'

'Well, you do seem to be stuck halfway from somewhere to nowhere, if you don't mind me saying,' said Smith. 'But what about Curious, don't you ever feel like going after her?'

'No, she's always done things like that ever since I've known her. I just wish I didn't allow myself to be persuaded by her all the time. Just can't help myself I suppose. Anyway, she will be all right, I'm sure. And I certainly don't see myself as 'stuck' here, as you say. Far from it. I'm very comfortable here. Could I expect anything more? No, I'm pleased where I am today and I intend to stay just where I am. Another coffee?'

'I believe that it's more a matter of realising our potential, not just satisfaction of our needs,' said Smith. 'I stand to deliver. I want to give better-than-excellent service. And in learning to do so I will receive greater-than-expected rewards.'

Habit turned from the view before him and looked confused.

'Better-than-excellent service?' Habit said. 'Why? In Familiar Town the service is what I've always been used to. Why would I want it to be any different?'

'Perhaps the service is better than the City of Apathy where I come from.'

'Well, I did visit that City once and I don't remember the service there being any different,' replied Habit.

'Then don't you mind poor service?' asked Smith.

'It's not a question of minding,' said Habit. 'It's a matter of what a person gets used to. Take me; I'm in the wholesale furnishing industry. We fulfil the orders for retail outlets. We don't have to worry about service too much though because of the system we operate.'

'What system?' enquired Smith.

'The order system of course,' answered Habit. 'Someone chooses a suite of furniture from a retail outlet. They pay something to secure it, although it doesn't actually exist yet. But their payment means we can start making it. Our system allows delivery to be between six and twelve weeks. Sometimes, because of a backlog of orders we don't start making it for twelve weeks. But the furniture doesn't take long to make and the customer doesn't seem to mind the extra time because they're just pleased to get it. Unless, of course, they get the wrong one or it's not been put together properly. But even if that happens the system always allows them to change it, though there would be a further waiting period.'

'And are your customers happy with that system?' asked Smith.

'I don't know. Anyway, even if they do complain I don't see how it would be down to us. It is down to the order takers. Our job is to meet the orders, not take them.'

'But surely the order takers liaise with you?'

'What and lose their sale!' exclaimed Habit. 'Why would they want to do that? That wouldn't help the industry would it, and with it getting so competitive it's hard enough as it is. Anyway, why should the customer complain? We make furniture that sells anyway. The customer doesn't have to buy. Another coffee?'

'But in following that system you risk having no customers,' said Smith.

'There will always be customers!' replied Habit. 'That is not the difficulty today. No, the difficulty comes when they challenge the way things are done. Things for which they should be grateful.'

'What do you mean exactly?' asked Smith.

'Take my friend, Routine,' said Habit. 'Now, *he* understands all about how important business is to customers. He's a bank manager. He has quite rightly got his customers to accept that they need the services his bank provides. But would you believe that some customers have argued that the bank needs them! How can a bank need them, after all it's the bank that has the money people want, not the other way about.'

'Well, it's an interesting concept, though I can't say I agree with you,' said Smith. 'Let's face it the bank wouldn't exist without customers.'

'You may say that, but I don't like upsetting my bank. If I did I would probably not be able to get any money out of one of those wall machines just when I needed it. *Anyway*, the point I'm making is that Routine received numerous complaints from customers who claimed they had been overcharged or treated unfairly in their loans. Naturally he ignored them, and most of the complaints went away over time, but this didn't satisfy one disgruntled customer. Routine told me that the customer visited the head office. Apparently some bright spark informed the customer that he could be reimbursed.'

'So what happened,' asked Smith. 'Did Routine apologise?'

'Far from it,' said Habit. 'And the customer closed his account and went elsewhere. Which goes to show that we need banks more than they need us. Another coffee?'

□   □   □

SMITH COULDN'T BE BOTHERED TO REASON with Habit. 'If I wasn't so tired I would,' he thought. And the longer Smith stayed in the Comfort Zone with Habit the more reluctant he felt about getting started again. Weary after his initial climb and so relaxed looking at the view, he fell asleep. As he did so his Charter fell from his jacket and rolled away. When he woke up he saw he was alone and that it was already early evening.

'How could I have been so stupid to rest for so long?' he chastised himself. 'It will be dark before I get to the top now and I still have to find House Integrity.'

Driven more by annoyance with himself than anything else, he was nearing the top when he met Suspicion and Criticism making their way down as fast as they could. 'Why are you going down in such a hurry?' he asked.

'Because the way ahead is dangerous, so there is little point in going there,' replied Suspicion

'But this is the way to Integrity House, isn't it?' asked Smith, 'what are you running away from?'

'Two infamous bandits, Bureaucrat and Administrate,' said Suspicion. 'We suspect they are on the rampage tonight.'

'And we don't want to get tangled up with them,' added Suspicion. 'Might I ask why you are about so late in the day? Are you a scout for them?'

'Of course not!' shouted Smith, nervously. 'I am on my way to House Integrity, but I fell asleep in the Comfort Zone.'

'Then you'll hardly be welcome at Integrity House. They don't have time for sluggards like you,' said Criticism. 'You'd better turn back.'

'And you should ask yourself why these outrageous bandits lie so close to Integrity House. Perhaps they are all in business together, eh?' added Suspicion.

'But how can you be certain these bandits are loose?' asked Smith.

'Do we look stupid?' said Suspicion continuing to make his way down the hill. 'A person has to be on their guard you know.'

'And it seems to me you're not much good at that,' added Criticism, following behind him.

Smith was left alone feeling afraid about what lay ahead. Furthermore, he felt discouraged about his whole trip. So, looking for some encouragement from his Charter, he felt for it in his coat. 'It's not there! How could I have been so careless as to lose it?' Realising he must have dropped it when he was in the comfort zone; he started to make his way back to it. 'How stupid of me! Now I will have to retrace my steps three times!'

◻   ◻   ◻

WHEN HE REACHED THE COMFORT ZONE he frantically searched around the area. Nothing. 'It must be nearby,' he thought and trying to stay calm, he searched again, methodically. His efforts paid off and with relief he found his Charter, seized it, and read its contents.

Reminding himself of his mission encouraged him and he set off up the hill again with a determined pace. 'I will not be put off my road, just because of what someone says,' he told himself. 'If there is danger ahead, then I will deal with it when I come to it!'

It was dark when Smith reached the top of the hill for the second time and he again chastised himself. 'I have missed the opportunity of seeing the view from up here as well as arriving at Integrity House in the safety of daylight.'

In the distance he could make out a clear light and immediately made towards it. As he did so he heard some distressed cries.

'I must be brave,' he encouraged himself, 'and keep going. It's not far now. I'll be there in just a short time'

Finally he saw an entrance and was relieved to see above it the sign Integrity House. At the same time the shouts were becoming louder. They were cries for help. Straining his eyes to see further down the entrance he could just make out two figures.

'Well, faint heart never served anyone,' he muttered and went closer.

'Help us,' said Bureaucrat, 'my colleague and I have been caught in a trap.'

Smith could now see that the person who spoke and his colleague were stuck in what appeared to be a tangle of red tape.

'You are indeed,' said Smith, 'but I think that it is of your own making. So, tell me how you think I can help you for I suspect that doing so will only leave me as tied up as you are.'

'That's what I told him when he asked me to help!' cried Administrate. 'The fool used far too much tape, much more than was necessary…'

'Be quiet, you idiot!' cursed Bureaucrat. 'If it wasn't for your bungling supervision this would never have happened!' And turning to Smith said in more pleasant terms. 'Help me to help you. I can assure you that it is within my power to smooth the way ahead for you.'

'And under what authority would that be?' enquired Smith.

'Under the authority invested in me by the State of Limbo, the region that lies ahead of you and one that you indeed may have to cross.'

'And I would be more than happy to arrange a transit visa and pass for you,' added Administrate, 'for a small fee, of course, though I am more than happy to discount this for you in return for your assistance.'

'You have clearly been hoisted by your own petard,' mused Smith, 'and I wonder how much of this red tape you were intending to use to entrap me. I'll tell you what I will do. As you are have wrapped yourself up near Integrity House, and I know that I alone could not free you, I will inform the residents straightaway. They will know what to do.'

'Wait,' called Bureaucrat, as Smith left them and walked towards the house. Ignoring their pleas, Smith knocked on the door.

□   □   □

INSIDE INTEGRITY HOUSE SMITH MET with Probity, who lived there with his two sisters, Prudence and Patience. After being welcomed, Smith apologised for being late and explained why. He then related the predicament of Bureaucrat and Administrate.

'I admit to being afraid when I met them, after I learned that they were bandits,' said Smith.

66

'Certainly, they are infamous for preying on the nerves of people,' replied Probity. 'But they are not really bandits.'

'But you were right to leave them, as we will do, for a while,' said Patience. 'For they must learn to stop delaying people who visit here.'

'Yes, we'll free them in the morning,' added Prudence. 'Though it won't be the first time, and certainly not the last.'

'But it *is* good to hear that you confronted your fears and in doing so overcame them,' said Probity. 'Having courage is not the absence of fear, it is having command over it.'

'And the more you face what frightens you, the more command you have,' said Patience.

'And the more honest you are about why you are afraid, the more you are able to face what frightens you,' added Prudence. 'But come now, it's late and you must be hungry and tired. Tomorrow we can talk.'

□   □   □

FULLY REFRESHED FROM A GOOD NIGHT'S SLEEP, Smith joined his three hosts.

'Good morning,' said Probity brightly. 'You'll be interested to know that we've freed your *acquaintances* from last night. Not that they realise it yet as they are both still fast asleep.'

'Yes, it's always easier that way,' joined in Prudence. 'Otherwise we only put ourselves at risk. They always seem to be intent on tying us up in knots.'

'They'll wake up when they're good and ready and plan what they're going to do next,' said Patience. 'They always do.'

'So,' said Probity, gazing at Smith, 'I take it that you are heading towards Service City?'

'Yes, though I have a lot to learn before getting there,' said Smith.

'And why is that?' asked Probity.

'Well, even after my time with Accountability, I allowed myself to get stuck in The Comfort Zone. I lacked the strength of mind to argue with Habit and I almost lost the Charter that Inspiration had instructed me to keep safe.'

'You are human, not a machine, and will learn through your mistakes. It takes time to build new habits that ensure success of your mission. You must learn to forgive yourself,' said Patience.

'It's important that you keep your mind on what *is* important to you,' added Probity, 'and in fairness you took action as soon as you realised your error. You went back to retrieve what was important and were rewarded by finding it.'

'And that was after you had met with Criticism and Suspicion,' said Prudence. 'They often loiter near the summit of Reluctance trying to put fear and doubt into aspiring agents. You were lucky they were in a hurry, because the tongues of those two can be more damaging than the danger they warned lay ahead of you.'

'But you *are* now here, said Probity, 'and *here* you will learn that the function of integrity is to reflect the beliefs, values and principles of every individual, both personally and professionally.'

'And with this ability you will be able to look upon people like Habit with tolerance, said Patience. 'We have heard of Habit too, and although he appears stuck in his ways there are good things about him. After all, however he was persuaded, he *has* made it half way up the Heights of Reluctance.'

'He was persuaded by his girlfriend, Curious,' said Smith.

'It usually does take an outside influence for Habit to do something different,' replied Patience, 'Unfortunately it is rarely permanent, unless he is able to decide for himself. Changing something about ourselves because we want to will always be of more benefit to us than changing because someone else has persuaded us. Once Habit no longer feels satisfaction for what he is doing or where he is, he will want to alter his view of things to seek greater satisfaction.'

'So, he will be able to change then and move forward?' asked Smith.

'It depends on the level of satisfaction that he gets for continuing to do what he does. If he is unsure as to whether his satisfaction will increase, then he will prefer to stick to what he knows. If what he is familiar with starts to give him more pain than pleasure, then the chances of him replacing an old tendency with a new one are good.'

'What Habit does is a reaction, though he thinks it is just instinctive,' said Probity. 'His reactions are because of repetition. That is why so much of what he does is second nature. It has become so through repetition. Now repetition in itself is neither a bad thing, nor a good thing. It is a learning tool but most of the time people use it to debilitate themselves rather than use it for growth.'

'Take imagination, for example,' said Prudence. 'It is at our disposal to create our dreams. Yet, many people misuse it for the disposal of their dreams.'

'But how can imagination bring about our dreams?' asked Smith.

'Because nothing can be materially accomplished without first being mentally created, so if we can learn to use it more proactively, instead of reactively, we benefit enormously. When repetitively used, imagination actually makes our dreams more real, more concrete. Conversely, and if we allow it, our fears become more real too.'

'Then we need to keep our mind on what we want to happen, instead of fretting over what we don't want to happen,' said Smith.

'Correct,' said Prudence.

'But what about Habit's friend Routine,' said Smith. 'He was particular about keeping his mind and actions on what he believed to be right, even at the expense of actually losing a customer.'

'People will always feel secure when they have a set format to follow,' replied Probity. 'Indeed, some will consider the security of everything they hold dear in the comfort of a traditional policy. That is why some people look to point out where others go wrong in not adhering to such a policy. Why, some will even take pleasure in it. Routine was misguided at the outset by one of the commonest myths in offering service to others. He put his own interests, and what he perceived as his bank's interests, before the interests of one of his customers. Integrity, however, requires putting your customer's interests before your own.'

□   □   □

'I REALLY BELIEVE THAT,' SAID SMITH. 'Yet businesses that claim to put customers first, seldom seem to follow through.'

'That's usually because as a marketing initiative it sounds good, and of course works in the short term,' said Probity. 'The reality is that such promises cause resentment when they remain undelivered. Integrity, in the individual or company, must be reflected in the service actions that make customers feel really valued. And in order to be able to deliver profitable service to the customer, it is important to show them that you value what they want more than you value what you do. Both their time and their interest are more important than your time and interests. In which case, you have to know what is important to you.'

'I know what is important to me,' said Smith. 'My customers are important to me and I stand to deliver what they want.'

'Those are fine words and the enthusiasm you recite them with makes me believe that you will follow them through,' said Probity. 'Customers don't like being let down when they have been promised that something will happen. They resent being told how fantastic a particular service is, yet then have to wait for it, and then being told that such a service is worth waiting for. They feel duped when exciting advertisements offer fantastic service and they are unable to get through on the phone, or when they do, the person on the other end is too busy, indifferent, disinterested, unaware of the offer, new at the job, offhand or even rude.

'Integrity is delivering what you promise, saying what you mean and meaning what you say. Everyone that serves another must be aware of the values that are important to him or her and the values that are important to the company. They can then put in genuine emotions into showing the customers how much they value them.'

'You have already learned that to give better-than-excellent service, there must be continuous improvement of the individual through personal development,' said Patience.

'I have indeed,' said Smith. 'And the importance of aligning what you are with what you do through evaluating motives and establishing a personal mission.'

'Then you understand that fulfilling your aim of giving better-than-excellent service is not just something to be ticked off on a to do list.'

'Absolutely, and I understand that my potential is realised through my commitment to continually stretching myself with challenging goals,' replied Smith.

'Well here lies the difficulty that business does not fully recognise when it promises to put customers first. Although every aspiring agent that seeks entry into Service City has a personal responsibility to work at being the best they can be, every business has a fundamental responsibility to do something too. Every business must school character.'

'What do you mean, school character?' asked Smith.

'The majority of people spend a greater portion of their life at work than school,' continued Patience. 'School teaches us many of life's basics, but it is not until we are interacting with others that we are able to hone and improve our basic skills, discover and utilise many others and have the opportunity to become what we are capable of.

'Our biggest growth will always come from our character development, but it is our competency that business is more interested in. Consequently, training budgets favour competency skills in the belief that greater competency will bring about greater profit. Business prefers systems to initiative. Most meetings are about improving the systems. Occasionally when under pressure to do something about poor communication, business may consider some character schooling, do it and then tick it off as done.

'The secret is to become a learning organization, providing the opportunity to continually improve people. In this way business ensures loyal customers, profitable growth and a harmonious working environment. The duty to treat employees as valued customers so they in turn duplicate such ethos with customers, is common to all business leaders in Service City.'

'I wish that it were the case where I come from,' said Smith. 'But this type of suggestion would be met with the concern that business would merely be training people to leave and start in competition against them.'

'There is a tendency for that viewpoint whenever the idea, action or follow through for this type of schooling is half-hearted or given lip service,' said Probity. 'People will not buy into something unless they can see that what is offered is for the benefit of all, and not just good for the business. Conducted properly, a business can stay unified with loyal employees who enjoy success because of their unified efforts. In so doing, success is continuously built on the success of others. Just imagine for a moment the vast resources of untapped potential within the members of a company. Without developing the confidence for people to do what they are truly capable off a business is not releasing its potential.'

'In my City many businesses tell their employees that they are its greatest asset, but the employees don't really believe it,' said Smith.

'Employees are not the greatest asset of a business,' said Probity.

'Then what is it?' asked a perplexed Smith.

'Why, customers of course!' said Probity. 'Without customers a business cannot exist. Cash flow is not the life blood of a business, customers are, for without them there is no cash flow, there is nothing.'

'So when a business fails it is not because of cash flow, then, it's because of lack of custom, said Smith.

'If you don't provide what people want, then no amount of cash flow will help,' put in Prudence. 'Often people will produce something and then try and market it, blaming marketing and poor sales for bad performance. After all, they will say, we know the product is good. The product may be the best invention since sliced bread, but if every customer around you prefers rice, what good will it do? What is required is a full understanding of what customers want to experience, a true empathy for them. Take quality, which can only ever be subjective. Many businesses pride themselves on the quality of the service they provide. But customers don't buy because of quality. They buy because of the quality they *perceive* they are getting.'

'So, understanding what customers want is about learning to understand how *they*, the customer, perceive things,' said Smith.

'Exactly!' said Probity, 'and this is a major point to understand, because perceptions relate to people's frame of reference. Our perceptions dictate how we react or respond to the things we see or are offered. They influence our values and beliefs, which is why it is important for business to see things in the same way that their customers do.'

'How is it possible to do that, though?' asked Smith.

'By putting yourself in their shoes,' answered Probity. 'Take any hotel in Service City for example. All the people who are involved must experience the hotel as a customer. Both the engineer and the housekeeper will then know at first hand if the shower unit really works, as it should. The receptionist will know what it is like to make a reservation, be put on hold, called back, assisted and welcomed. The cashiers will experience first hand what it is like when they come to settle a bill. The restaurant employees will experience what it is like to book, wait, be served, eat and be treated. All personnel will acquire an understanding of what it is like *to be* a

74

customer at their hotel. They will be able to perceive as the customer does, and in so doing, will perceive their role and the customer's role more clearly.'

'But surely they would get different treatment anyway because they work there and their colleagues would be conscious of why they are there,' said Smith. 'And how could they be expected to pay for their stay when it was for the sake of the customer?'

'Well, first there is an understanding between hotels in Service City so that employees can stay at different hotels and find out what it is like to be a customer. What they experience assists their perception of the customer experience. When they stay at their own hotel their experience will then tell them if they are getting special treatment, or if the service is the way it always is. Also, colleagues recognise the importance of the learning experience so everyone benefits. Secondly, it is a proven fact that people do not value anything that they receive for nothing. The hotels in Service City therefore provide an additional allowance for character development, such as learning the customer experience, which is considered extremely valuable. The employee does not have to use it, but in doing so, it is a clear indication that he or she shares the values that the hotel stands by.'

'So understanding the customer experience is something that hotels in Service City highly value,' said Smith.

'It is certainly considered the vital key in developing long lasting loyal relationships with the growing number of clientele.'

'I can't wait to experience such service,' said Smith. 'The last few hotels that I stayed in were so busy dealing with customers they never had time to serve them. Some do make an effort to do what they can. But it is based on their perception of what should be done, rather than on their experience of what could be done.

'I recall my own experience at a hotel where I once commented that the shower in my en-suite room was not functioning correctly. Though they appreciated the information and promised to repair it, the next time I stayed there I discovered the same thing in a different room. When I asked at reception if all the rooms were perhaps the same, I was told that the engineers were always complaining that housekeeping never kept them informed of difficulties. But reception would pass on the comment anyway.'

'Then you see the importance of character development in addition to competency,' said Probity, 'and the importance of perceiving what the customer wants through understanding their experience; and of not putting your own interests before those of whom you are serving.

'It was the aim of our father, Integrity and our mother, Trust, that these elements should be at the very core of both individual and organisational values. They considered that the best way to show your customers how much you value them was through keeping whatever promises you made to them. My sisters and I are committed to sharing these values with aspiring agents intent on becoming operatives with Secret Service. For we, like our parents, acknowledge that gaining the rewards of success and wealth requires greater adherence to such values, because of the additional responsibility that such rewards bring with them.'

'I am grateful for your generous hospitality,' said Smith. 'And I promise that I will apply the wisdom you have shared with me.'

'Your sincerity is clearly genuine,' said Probity getting up and walking towards the door, 'and, though you have a long way ahead, you are now well prepared and have a strong resolve. Come, sisters, let us walk with our guest to beyond our gate.'

<<< AGENT SMITH FILE NOTE >>>

1. Inspire yourself with what you stand for.

2. Beware of habits that distract you from your path.

3. Always face up to what frightens you.

4. Keep your mind on what is important to you.

5. put your customer's interests before your own.

6. Change via personal choice rather than external pressure.

7. Use imagination to keep your inspirations achievable.

8. Value your customer's time more than you value your own.

004

Conquering the Valleys of Discontent

SMITH WAS CAREFUL TO WATCH HIS STEP; his determination fuelled by sighting Good Fortune from the summit of Reluctance. Able to see where he was going had increased his resolve to get there. As he entered the Valley of Outer Discontent, the aspiring agent said out loud: 'I am lucky to know where I am going!'

'That depends on where you *ought* to be going,' said a voice to his side. 'What the hell do you think you are doing so far from where you *should* be?'

Turning quickly to the clearing at his side Smith was horrified to see a hideous creature. Its skin tensed in knots; eyes without emotion; and arms to crush anything that came too close.

'Stay away from me, whatever you are!' shouted Smith in alarm.

'Now that's not very grateful of you after I have gone out of my way to find you,' snarled Security-itas. 'Where have you come from and where are you going?'

Fear rose in Smith's mind as he realised that the creature in front of him was the exact one he had hoped *not* to meet. Overcoming his fear, Smith said, 'I have recently left the City of Apathy within the State of Mediocrity and I am heading towards Prosperity.'

'What gives you the nerve to make such a trip and to leave without my permission?' snapped Security-itas. 'Don't you know that I rule the State of Mediocrity 'If it wasn't for my expectation that you will return to me, I

79

would strike you down now! But I invite you to come back to my State of your own free will and I promise to reward you with greater privileges than you would ever receive in Prosperity. You have no idea how the realms of my State can benefit you over time.'

'Ah, but I do,' said Smith. 'Because I have known many of your subjects and without exception they have lost the will to rule themselves.'

'Of course and why would *I* want it to be any different!' said Security-itas, 'for what better way is there? I rule them and in the knowledge that I do, they find comfort. Make no mistake security is what *everyone* wants and *I* am the only one who can provide it.'

'The only security you offer is a false sense of security,' argued Smith defiantly. 'One that only results in making a person insecure.'

'Rubbish! How can you believe such a thing? Whenever people want the security of a status, title or role, I give it to them. Whenever they want security in the form of possessions, a car, or better house, I give it to them. What other ruler does that? Come, take the opportunity to return to my State before it is too late.'

'Opportunity? How can the security you talk about be an opportunity?' scoffed Smith. 'Nothing external can ever provide a permanent sense of security. Reliance for what lies outside of us can only ever grow insecurity. To my mind, only a firm resolve to fulfil my potential can provide meaningful security for me.'

'Ha!' snarled Security-itas. 'What resolve? Is that the resolve that got you stuck in Procrastination? Is that the resolve that drove you to continuously ask others how to get of frustration, when all you had to do was ask me? Is that the resolve that caused you to fall asleep so easily in The Comfort Zone? To lose your Charter almost as soon as you were given it? To consider turning back when bandits were ahead of you? Ha! Some resolve! Do you think that this Prosperity you talk of will be impressed by your 'resolve'? Why don't you just stop deluding yourself! Now, do I make such demands of you? Not at all! All *I* ask is for you to *not* try to be someone you're *not*. Why do you think I have come searching for you?'

'Because you gain your own power from the insecurities of men!' said Smith. 'It may be true that my resolve was not firm at the outset but that was because until recently I didn't know myself, didn't know my capabilities, let alone even believe in myself.

'Under your rule I never even considered evaluating myself or really understanding what my motives could possibly be. I was too busy evaluating others in case they threatened my security. I had no real idea about what was important to me, or indeed what I stood for. I was more concerned about evaluating others so that I could get a handle on them. But that was before I realised that you can only truly recognise the motives of others when you are sure of your own. And I don't believe that my future is simply an extension of my past. Just because I have made mistakes, does not make me a mistake. Just because I have failed, does not make me a failure.

'In pursuing my course my resolve has become firmer, my belief in myself is stronger, my confidence in myself is greater. My self-respect and integrity are my security now and the only security I'll ever need. That is what is asked of me to reach Service City, because the Founder there, Customer, knows that with Secret Service I am able to serve others to the best of my ability. Living under your rule offers no more than becoming my own worst enemy!'

Security-itas exploded, 'I despise the ideas that you have been brainwashed with. This *Customer* you talk of is a false ruler, one that demands a sense of freedom in place of servility. How can people feel secure if they are free to do what they want for others? Without confinement there can only be anarchy. Such philosophy can only threaten my existence, which I will not tolerate!'

Smith could see that the time to fight the menace before him had finally come. Security-itas was intent on destroying his ideas with ice-cold doubt and Smith began to feel a rising sense of panic inside him.

The fearsome onslaught continued for half a day and, despite almost everything inside screaming at him to give up, Smith kept his ground. Then, as if sensing Smith was nearing exhaustion, Security-itas struck a vicious blow: 'Look at you! You are giving up, just as expected!' shouted Security-itas in triumph.

Drawing on his last ounce of resolve Smith faced up to the destroyer of dreams, 'I will never give up to you,' he said firmly. 'My resolve is the measure of my belief in myself! And it doesn't involve you.'

Security-itas at last halted his spiteful onslaught and with a parting look of venomous resentment fled. Never to be seen by Smith again.

Smith did not know how long he lay exhausted. As he began to come around he felt nauseous and ached all over. Physically, emotionally and mentally drained, he realised: 'I have finally come face to face with the monster that most frightened me into giving up on my mission! It almost overcame me but I defeated it!'

He sensed an inner calm that he had not experienced before.

'How ridiculous to have previously concerned myself with what other people think of me? How can it be any of my business what others think? I can't get inside their head. The frame of reference that dictates how they may perceive me is not within my control. There is only one thing in my control and that is *my* thinking. How can I control their thinking? What right have I got to do so anyway?

'It is *so* clear to me now that at any one time each of us is either in control of our lives, or not in control of it. There are no halfway measures. Whenever I react to someone because what they say bothers me, I am giving them control over my emotions. Whenever I do not react to what they say, but respond to what I feel is right, guided by what is important to me, I maintain command over my thinking.

'If I can't control my thinking what is my life worth? If I can't have command over my thoughts how will I have command over my actions? My security is having confidence in what I do and belief in my will to do it. It is in knowing what I want, and keeping my thoughts on what I want. If I hadn't been so concerned about meeting Security-itas, it would never have challenged me in the first place.

□   □   □

FEELING STRONGER, SMITH CONTINUED ONCE MORE. A short time later he saw that the road ahead led into another valley, deeper and darker than the one he was crossing. As he approached, he noticed two figures following a path that skirted around this darker valley. When the first of them, whose name was Liquidate, arrived at where the path joined he noticed Smith and waited for him.

'You don't want to think about going down there,' he said.

'Why ever not?' asked Smith.

'Because it is the Valley of Inner Discontent,' said the other, named Bankrupt, who now caught up. 'Few who enter are ever able to get through.'

'But it looks as if you have both just passed through,' said Smith.

'We haven't actually gone through the middle of it,' said Bankrupt. 'We had each been skirting the edge of it, trying to find a way through, when we met up with each other.'

'Mind you,' added Liquidate, 'just doing that was a dreadful experience.'

'Though you must admit that we have both grown from the experience,' said Bankrupt. 'And if we hadn't both been trying to get through we would not have met up with each other, which has not made us feel so alone as we did before, has it?'

'It is true that you will feel less alone when meeting someone who has travelled the same path,' said Smith. 'But tell me where have you come from and where are you going.'

'Well,' began Liquidate, 'I have come a long way and, it would seem, I still a long way to go. That's if I can ever get out of these infernal Valleys of Discontent. I'm originally from Façade Town in State Ploy. I had a company selling financial services. It's what made our town what it was, but what none of us fully realised was that everyone was in the same business. We were all selling services, but there were no real products being manufactured. It came to the point that everyone could only sell futures, or derivatives, for nothing really existed.

'However', Liquidate continued, 'borrowing was easy and following the philosophy that if you could act the part, you would get more business, we borrowed more. That way we could buy all the trappings of success and, of course, market ourselves more. Anyway, initially the business went from strength to strength, well, at least we thought it did. We were seen at all the right places with all the right people and the media started writing about us as *the* company to watch. Perhaps in hindsight we believed our own propaganda because, before we realised it, we were way over extended. And by that time it was too late and we had to close the company. I'm now on my way to the New Settlement in the State of Limbo to see what advice I can get from the Administrators there.'

'Perhaps it would be better if you by-passed there and set off towards Service City,' suggested Smith.

'But I don't need to go there, as there is nothing about service that I am looking to learn,' replied Liquidate. 'And I am sure there is no industry that understands better than ours what good service is. No, what I need is to be able to start again so that I can win back the respect of my peers. It's so embarrassing not having the trappings of success I used to have.'

'Well, at least you kept your home,' said Bankrupt. 'At least you didn't lose all your personal money. You just lost your company. No doubt creditors lost out more than you did. I lost everything! Listening to you makes me wonder that just because we found ourselves on the same road, we are perhaps not such kindred spirits as I first hoped.'

'Maybe by skirting the Valley you are not facing what you really should be facing about yourself,' offered Smith. 'Possibly you may benefit from passing through it'

'There's no way that I'm ready to pass through there,' replied Liquidate, 'and I don't see why I should have to anyway. It may be that creditors lost more than I did, but at least their good name didn't suffer, as mine has. Anyway that was a risk they took, after all they only invested in me because they thought they were on to a good thing!'

'They more than likely invested in you because they believed in you,' said Smith. 'But either way they were still your customers in effect. You had a duty to serve them to the best of your ability. It strikes me that you used their investment to serve your own ends.'

'Who are you to judge me?' shouted Liquidate.

'I wasn't in the least bit judging you,' said Smith calmly. 'I was looking at your story from my own point of view. Your story indicates to me that you believe your predicament is not your fault.'

'It isn't! And it's grossly unfair that this has happened,' said Liquidate.

'Yet, in business we must recognise who our customers are, and we must make it our personal responsibility to serve them as much through choice, as duty,' said Smith. 'The investors and shareholders of your company were as much customers as those clients were that you advised on their finances. Both provided money in return for the service that you must have promised them. Otherwise why would they invest with you?'

'Because the *company* promised them, not me,' said Liquidate.

'But you *were* the company. You formed it so it was merely an extension of you,' said Smith. 'Taking personal responsibility is not about hiding behind legal documents. Since when can a legal document take the place of integrity? You must ask yourself why you went into business. Was it to make money out of your clients, or for your clients? Was it for the accolade of what being in business would bring you, or for the benefits that you could bring to others because of it?'

'Look, I just did what everybody does and unluckily it didn't work out for me,' said Liquidate. 'But I'm going to make sure I have a stronger base next time. Now, if you'll both excuse me, I must make my way to New Settlement.'

As Liquidate got up to leave, Smith said, 'If you insist on going the way I have just come I strongly urge you to make your way directly out of this valley, for at the top you will find Integrity House.'

'Thank you, but I'm bound for the State of Limbo before I do anything else,' replied Liquidate.

'Then if that's the case you may discover that you meet up with two people that suit you anyway,' offered Smith. 'Both are from that State and one of them is always keen to provide a pass to get you there.'

□   □   □

AS HE WATCHED HIS FORMER TRAVELLING companion leave, Bankrupt said, 'Perhaps because of my current despair I latched on to someone who made me feel as though I wasn't alone in my predicament.'

'It is natural to seek either motivation or solace in people we believe to be like-minded individuals,' said Smith. 'But whenever we are vulnerable we must be careful about what think we need. What we perceive to be like-minded behaviours and attitudes that fit in with our individual preferences and desires, can in reality turn out to be an complete anathema to us.'

'You know, there were a couple of occasions when I was strongly inclined to enter into the valley below,' said Bankrupt. 'Then, when I met with my recent companion, I became less inclined to enter.'

'It is better to follow our strong inclinations than passively submit to the environment that surrounds us,' said Smith. 'But tell me what's your tale? How did you come to be here in the first place?'

'I am from the Zone of Enterprise not far from here,' began Bankrupt. 'Though I did have a goal to visit Service City, my overriding goal was to get started in business on my own account. Then, when I had made it, I was going to visit there in style. But I always believed in the stories that I'd heard from people who had been there.'

'What stories?' asked Smith inquisitively.

'That the secret to winning and keeping customers is to reward them,' said Bankrupt. 'And that the most important customer to win over is yourself, because the best salesperson is the true believer.'

'If you have been fortunate to learn such things, how did you come to lose everything?' asked Smith.

'Well, perhaps it was because a little knowledge is a dangerous thing or because to know and not to do is still not to know,' replied Bankrupt. 'Though, I admit that someone told me that only *after* I had lost everything. The point was, though, that I did believe in the products that I was selling. At first things went brilliantly, but as my success grew, for some reason I began to imagine that it couldn't last. I then started to lose my earlier confidence in winning sales. Then I began to worry about the competition. There was so much of it you know. It's odd because I'd never been aware of how much when I first started out.

'Then I began thinking that my prices might be too high. So I decided to make my products the cheapest available. That seemed to do the trick at first because, with all focus on sales, we sold loads of products. Of course, we weren't able to provide the same after sales service, but that didn't seem to matter because we could hardly keep up with the demand as it was. Then they stopped selling again. So I reduced the prices again, but still they wouldn't sell. I thought it was because the market was saturated; but another competitor's products, that were all but identical to mine, were still selling well and at a *higher* price!

'It became so desperate that I had to put *everything* I had into just keeping going, but the more I pushed customers as to the attraction of what they were buying, the less they wanted to know. Eventually, I had to close down, hardly got anything for all the stock I was left with and well, you know the rest.'

'Where are you heading now?' asked Smith.

'Well, nowhere in particular. Since my world fell apart I've been stuck in this valley,' Bankrupt said as he motioned around him. Then pointing at the darkness below him added, 'and I've already told you that there's been a couple of times when I've wandered into that dark valley below. But the first time I came out quickly because I felt an immense fear of failure to get through to the other side.'

'Sometimes we must go where our leaning takes us, as it is the best way for each of us to grow,' consoled Smith. 'Because I am not as close to what has happened to you, as you are, I see things differently. It seems to me that even though your fear was groundless; you allowed it to fuel insecurity in your original belief about what you were doing. Only by passing through that valley below, will you be able to face such fear and in doing so defeat it.'

'But who wants to go through Inner Discontent?' said Bankrupt. 'Look at it; the wood is so thick in that valley down there that you can hardly see the trees. Even if a person were to enter, how would they ever be sure about coming out the other side?'

'The path must go through the wood because you can see how this one and several others lead right up to it,' said Smith.

'Then why don't we pass through it together, side by side?'

'Well, for one thing the path doesn't look wide enough for even one person to pass by, let alone for two to go side by side,' said Smith. 'And for another thing I don't believe that our paths are one and the same.'

'What do you mean by that?' enquired Bankrupt.

'Simply that I am confident about where I am heading, whereas you are still recovering from where you are coming from,' replied Smith.

'But you just said that the best thing for me was to pass through that valley?' said Bankrupt.

'Yes, because I believe that you must face your fear, but you cannot do that with me. Nor can I with you. It is something we must each face alone. Entering together will only cause us to rely on each other and in doing so we would only be borrowing the strength of the other. We must take the opportunity to build our own strength of character by passing through it in our own way, taking our own path. It is not wise to rely too much on the strength of another, as we may not always be with another in times of difficulty.'

'Well, if you forgive me,' said Bankrupt quietly, 'I'll rest here a little while longer first. What you say is right, it's just that you look so prepared and confident.'

'Because of your recent experiences you are probably better prepared than I,' replied Smith. 'Indeed, having lost everything as you have, you are in a stronger position than I am. You have everything to gain. The route ahead may well be the kindred spirit you require right now, helping you to emerge with confidence in yourself once more. It may even be one that you could not have taken were it not for your experiences. As for my part, I am not certain what I must face for I have not lost everything as you have.'

'Maybe not, but I get the feeling that you have been prepared to give up everything for what you believe in,' said Bankrupt.

'That may be one reason why our paths are different,' replied Smith.

'You know, when you refused my company a moment ago I resented you. Now that you have explained your reasons I realised that in refusing me you were actually giving me a greater service: the opportunity to stand on my own two feet. I will not forget your words of support. Good luck.'

□ □ □

ON APPROACHING THE VALLEY of the inner discontent, Smith felt an awful sense of foreboding. 'It is so dark and more overgrown than I thought. Perhaps there is a way around it after all? But what am I saying? That I want to spend forever skirting around here! Anyway, it cannot be worse than my meeting with Security-itas.'

Smith continued to talk to himself for confidence and as he did so he thought he could hear other voices. In time the valley became so dark that it became almost impossible to see the path ahead and he had to feel his way. With his vision unclear it appeared to Smith that his other senses were becoming more acute. On his hands and knees he felt for the ruts and pitfalls that randomly lay in his path. The voices he had heard seemed to now whisper persuasively in his ear. 'There's no point in biting off more than you can chew, you know?' said one, 'Give up on your empty mission.'

'You must realise that you're chasing rainbows,' laughed another, 'there's no such thing as good service. It's a pipe dream.'

'You're wasting your time with all this touchy-feely stuff,' sneered another, 'it doesn't work. You should be getting on with your job and stop wasting everyone's time.'

'And fancy leaving your family on their own!' criticised one, 'what sort of a person does that? Some responsibility that it is, letting them fend for themselves.'

'But I have to do this!' protested Smith. 'If a man doesn't follow what is important to him, what has he got?'

'Well, whatever he may have, he's going to lose,' a voice sneered. 'Why should anyone want to stay around someone who's so selfish? No one likes people who are only out for themselves, hiding behind some noble cause.'

'I'm not out for myself,' argued Smith, 'and I believe my cause is noble. I stand to deliver and I'm determined to discover the secrets of doing so.'

'Stop fooling yourself, *please*!' an exasperated voice sighed. 'Why don't you just simply know your place? You have a fine home and a good job, all this rocking the boat isn't going to do you any good at all.'

Smith argued with the voices and got angrier and angrier. The voices kept up their barrage, sometimes persuasive, sometimes sneering, and always patronising. In his blind anger Smith tripped into a particularly deep pit. Grabbing at the edge his legs swung in an empty void, while the voices that were now all around him laughed. With his life now at risk, his focus changed and he ignored the continual taunting of the voices suggesting that he just let go and give up the fight. 'There's no way I'm going to get stuck in this rut,' he shouted, as he slowly pulled himself up and out of danger.

'You see what happens when you do things you that are beyond you,' said a voice. 'At least you've had a go, now just accept that where you're hoping to go is not for the likes of you. Go back now, no one will be any the wiser. Otherwise you'll only fall again and what if you can't get out? Then what will you do?'

'Even though the way ahead is dark I can see what you are all about,' said Smith, realising that until now he had been fighting fire with fire. 'Do you think that I don't know who you are?'

'We only have your interests at heart you know,' answered a voice.

'Yes, we're only trying to protect you from yourself,' said another.

'It's better to know your place, really it is, for what good would it do if everyone went around doing their own thing?' said another.

'Thank you for your cautionary advice,' said Smith. 'But please forgive me if I choose not to heed it. For I realise *now* that there are many voices within us, but only one *true* one. You voices have no right to be here because you all belong to the *past*. I hold no malice towards you and indeed forgive you, for I accept the responsibility for your existence. Because, however, dormant you have been I have always kept you alive and given you any power you may have. Many of you I now recognise from my formative years when your admonishments were considered necessary to my development.

'I now admit to myself that I was simply duplicating what had been said to me when I was young. Echoes of words intended to control, rather than direct, spoken to me in childhood. Even though there have been times that I vowed to myself that I would never repeat what had been said to me, I confess there were days when I would catch myself saying it. With so many voices within us

93

giving us conflicting advice, no wonder it is nearly impossible to have unity within our mind.

'And you now taught me how to filter out those voices that do not resonate in harmony within me. It is to go deep into myself and feel the words that come to me and strike a chord of rightness. And the best way to do that is to talk calmly to myself and not in anger or fear. For I can confirm better how I really think about something when I hear myself say it out loud.

'Listening to you almost destroyed me. Your cautionary warnings that sowed seeds of doubt prove that affirmations work. But I now use affirmations for my benefit. With positive self-talk I will affirm to myself what is important to me. So, go away negative inner voices, your days are at an end.'

At those words Smith could at last see light at the end of the tunnel ahead of him. Within a few moments he was once more out in the open, this time standing in the bright rays of the morning sun. He realised that he had spent the whole night being subjected to the horrors of the dark valley.

□   □   □

AFTER A SHORT TIME SMITH CAME to the top of ridge where he surveyed the land for some way before him. Not too far away ahead was a solitary figure on the same road. Smith quickened his pace.

'Hey, wait for me!' shouted Smith.

Self-Reliance turned, stopped and waited for Smith to join him.

'Are you going to Prosperity and Service City?' asked Smith.

'Ah, I know Prosperity but I have never been to its capital, so I am heading there now,' said Self-Reliance.

Smith looked surprised, 'You know Prosperity, yet have not visited its capital? Forgive me asking, but why?'

'Well I was actually on my way but was falsely directed by Arrogance and Pride. I found myself where I had been much earlier, at the bottom of the Heights of Reluctance. As soon as I realised I politely made to leave their company. Pride was hurt and Arrogance argued how fortunate I had been to have met up with them in the first place and how dare I turn down their offer of a shortcut.'

'What happened?' said Smith with concern.

'Well, I knew that I would have to get away from their influence as quickly as possible when I realised they were intent on preventing me taking the right road so I began to Scale the Heights of Reluctance. They shouted at me to do as I was told if I knew what was good for me. Anyway, they were unable to catch me.

'Soon after that, I passed a pleasant spot and I was about to take a rest when I saw two people, a couple I think. Anyway, as it looked as though they were having a difference of opinion, and hadn't seen me, I thought it would be better to go on. Later, when I did rest, I looked back down at them. I could see that the woman was making her way back down the Hill, while the man was busy making himself a drink'.

'Coffee, no doubt,' put in Smith. 'That'll have been Habit and his girlfriend Curious. I never met *her* but I did talk with him and you were wise not to stop. As for me, I fell asleep there and was careless enough to lose my Charter. But tell me, was the view good from the top because it was dark when I reached it?'

'Well, actually there was not a great to deal to see because the summit was covered in cloud,' replied Self-Reliance. 'Mind you,' he added with amusement, 'it's not often I have my head in the clouds so it was a new

95

experience! But more seriously though, because I couldn't see ahead to my destination, I had the most overwhelming reluctance to continue on my travels. I felt as if I should just go back down and forget my recently forged quest.'

'Then I was lucky to reach the top at night after all,' said Smith. 'Though I was unfortunate to meet both Criticism and Suspicion and a couple of other rogues on the road at night.'

'I met with no one until I entered the first of the two valleys behind us,' said Self-Reliance quietly.

'Did you meet with Security-itas?' questioned Smith taking the opportunity to briefly share his own dreadful experience.

'No,' said Self-Reliance. 'Unfortunately I met with Hostility and Spite and my friendly manner did not go down at all well.'

'What gives you the right to be so confident and courteous?' Hostility said to me. 'Coming down into our valley with your airs and graces as if you own the place! Get out of here!'

'Well I was not going to be put off my course just because of some unfriendly words,' continued Self-Reliance. 'So I told him that this was the direction I was heading, that I was sorry if I had inadvertently offended him and that perhaps he'd tell me where I had gone wrong. His friend Spite whispered something to him and he became friendlier and went to one side to let me pass. As I did so they both tripped me up and ran off shouting, "that'll teach you for thinking you're better than we are!"'

'How awful!' said Smith, 'But why did they do it?'

'Because *they* believed that my manner threatened their security, and what people perceive as threatening, they attack,' said Self-Reliance.

'And what people perceive they allow to distort their beliefs, values and in turn their communications with others, of course,' offered Smith.

'Most people feel more threatened when someone appears to be different to the way they are. They feel insecure and don't know why,' said Self-Reliance.

'Hostility and Spite remind me of School bullies,' said Smith, 'there was always a crowd that used to enjoy poking fun at someone if that person was good at a particular subject. I wonder what the schools are like in Service City?'

'Well, from what I have heard about the emphasis on learning and consideration,' replied Self-Reliance, 'I imagine that each pupil develops their potential to the full.'

'And I bet they're taught how to succeed, rather than how to get by,' said Smith. 'Yes, I would like to send my children to a school like that.'

'One day all schools will be like that, though it may take a few generations,' said Self-Reliance. 'And I truly believe it will happen, for the ripples of this type of schooling already exist. I have seen them in my travels.'

'Tell me, did you meet with anyone else in the Valleys of Discontent?'

'Yes, I met with Disappointment,' said his companion. 'His story was sad to hear but after telling me about his life, he started on me. He told me it must have been a setback for me not to be able to stay in one place for long. He asked me if I knew the stress I must have caused my parents for always wanting to do my own thing. How trouble must have followed me throughout my life. That with the way I was going I could only ever expect hardship, misadventure and desolation.

'To say I felt crushed was an understatement,' continued Self-Reliance. 'Meeting with him gave me a sense of foreboding that I had not experienced before. But I was able to keep my wits about me and asked him why he didn't think about how he could helpful toward others. He seemed pleased that I had asked this question and told me that: "People don't generally like me. They will even cross the street to get away from me if they see me coming. Yet, if they took the time to just greet me and even asked how I came to be there, before they passed me by, as you have done, they would see that I am not so bad after all."

'Sort of meet him head on?' asked Smith.

'I believe that is what he was trying to say,' said Self-Reliance. 'But you must admit, I said to him, that you do have a tendency to make people feel depressed.'

'What did he say to that?' asked Smith.

'Well, it was odd because he told me that it wasn't *him* that made people melancholy. They did that to themselves simply because they weren't prepared to meet him face to face. He said their thoughts drew him towards them and then, when he appeared, to give them some guidance, they ran away from him. And with that he passed me by.'

'Reflecting on what he had said, I realised we have two choices in life. One is to remain happy whatever the outcome; and the other is to only be happy if the outcome is as we hoped for.'

'Well, certainly, the first choice is the obvious one,' said Smith.

'Of course, but almost all of us continue to choose the second. Yet by remaining unconcerned about our outcomes, as the first choice involves, we put ourselves in stronger command of our lives. And how could we better serve ourselves than having greater command over ourselves?'

'Which brings meaning to the principle of serving yourself first before serving others, for it is the best way to serve others!' said Smith. 'Serving yourself doesn't mean *taking* first, it simply means putting oneself in order first!'

'Which requires having command over yourself. Doing unto others as we would have them do unto us is fine so long as we learn to serve ourselves as the very special beings we are. But the reality is that people *treat* others the way they treat themselves, though they are seldom aware of it. The energy, for instance, that each of us employs in self-hurt, is the same energy that we use to hurt others. When we meet with a setback, our tendency is to want to take it out on others.'

'Then it seems to me, said Smith, 'that it is important for us to each learn how to overcome setbacks and rejection. Because it is not possible to be of service to others without this understanding.'

'Which means we must constantly try to extend ourselves,' said Self-Reliance. 'That way we bring about the greatest possible value that we can feel about ourselves as well as what we bring to others. For in truth it's not what we achieve, it's what we become.'

'Look!' said Smith, 'We've reached the ridge! At last we can leave Discontent behind us!'

<<< AGENT SMITH FILE NOTE >>>

1. Security is not found in the opinion of others.

2. Self-respect and self-belief is the only security.

3. Regularly affirm what you want to achieve.

4. You have to become before doing, and do before having.

5. Accept full responsibility for whatever happens to you.

6. Know where you are going so you recognise it upon arrival.

7. Trusting in your own counsel will banish doubt.

8. You command your life when unconcerned about outcomes.

9. Defeat what you fear by facing it head on.

005

SURVIVING SUPERFICIAL TOWN

'IT'S GOOD THAT YOU ARE TRAVELLING together at last.'

'Intuition!' said Smith, 'Well, it's good to come across you again. We were wondering what lay ahead.'

'Whatever it is you will perceive it differently than you used to,' replied Intuition. 'You now carry an air of conviction and self-belief in place of frustration, which tells me that you have emerged victorious in the battle of self-improvement.'

'We serve society through our aspirations rather than our frustrations,' said Smith, 'and to be the best we can be is the best way we can serve.'

'Well said! However, you are about to enter a sanctimonious place that will not appreciate this philosophy,' said Intuition. 'You must proceed with care through Superficial, the name of the town, as its Pretension Market has waylaid many aspiring agents.'

'How can somewhere like that exist on the route to Good Fortune?' asked Self-Reliance.

'There was a time when this road was incredibly crowded with people searching for Good Fortune. Superficial Town came into existence to meet the increasing demands of travellers who were no longer prepared to wait. The Town grew quickly as people were deceived into thinking that living there was much better than continuing on their journey. Rumours, started by self-interested individuals, like Judge Find-Fault, that to go on meant sacrificing everything for nothing, became rife. People were offered vanities in the form of possessions and pleasures in return for abandoning their dreams and staying to populate the town.

'It suited some people to stay because, though they knew what they wanted, they weren't prepared to pay the price to get it. Now, of course, those same people do not like it when others seem committed to going where they themselves were unable to go. It highlights their own inadequacies, so they try to prevent it using the same thing that prevented them: Pretension Market.'

'Must we go by that way?' enquired Smith. 'There must be another route?'

'Unfortunately at this point in your journey there is only one road before entering Good Fortune. It's as if all roads meet at this junction,' replied Intuition.

'Have you any advice before entering this town?' asked Self-Reliance.

'My advice has consistently been to be yourself. You now have a clear idea of who you are, where you are going and how to be yourself. But now that you exude confidence, the townspeople will instantly pick you out as not being one of them. They will see you as someone to be persuaded to stay, or, be destroyed.'

'Destroyed?' said Smith

'Unfortunately, your presence conflicts with what they have deluded themselves that they stand for,' answered Intuition. 'They will question you about your values and your inevitable replies will be viewed as a slight against the way they live.'

'But we would never want to put someone down,' argued Smith. 'So if we just keep to ourselves they might leave us alone.'

'Whatever you do to get through you must do in line with your values,' said Intuition. 'Just remember to keep your mind always on why you want to get through. You have already met and overcome Security-itas by keeping your resolve, haven't you?'

'Yes, I have, though I was tested to breaking point,' said Smith. 'And it seemed that the more I struggled, the stronger Security-itas seemed to get.'

'Because Security-itas drew strength from *your* fear, *your* doubts and *your* insecurities,' answered Intuition. 'It wasn't until you decided to *never* give up, no matter what, that Security-itas's rule over you was at an end.'

'The interesting thing was that the instant before I overcame Security-itas I saw the outcome in my mind's-eye and my action automatically followed through.'

'I think I know what you're saying,' said Self-Reliance. 'It's that sense of command that comes to you just at the precise moment when you are about to do something that scares, yet excites you and that you *feel* you can do and you follow it through.'

'It is true that many fine ideals have been forever lost simply because they have not been followed through,' said Intuition. 'The same applies with relationships. The lack of saying something when it should be said, or the *not* saying something when it shouldn't be said is damaging enough, but by far the main reason why relationships fail is because of lack of follow through.'

'I realise that marketing is not about selling, it's about building relationships,' said Smith. 'And the principle of trust is as applicable in any other relationship. Saying to my family that I'll do something and then not doing it, is no different to promising a customer and then not delivering. Whether one is family or not isn't the point. I would have raised the hopes of both and let them down.'

'My colleague Rationale,' said Intuition, 'would first defend your actions with your family by telling you that they'll understand and forgive you because you have to work. Then, he would defend your actions with the customer suggesting that they won't mind because no one ever calls back when they say they will anyway. The reality is, however imperceptible, both relationships are weakened.'

'Trust is created by demonstrating reliability, responsibility with communication,' put in Self-Reliance. 'Follow through service is generally not expected and rarely performed, but is tremendously appreciated. It is the small considerate acts of reassurance that develop people's confidence in you and build your reputation as trustworthy.'

'Close attention to details determines relationships,' said Intuition. 'Thoughtfulness costs less than thoughtlessness.'

'At Communication Limited we rely on voice-mail and electronic answers to customers' queries,' said Smith. 'Our call centres are so busy they often forget to do what has been requested, because the next call immediately follows. It is not considered critical because the customer can always call again.'

'You're right! As a student I worked in one of those call centres and the only training I got was during the first day on how many calls to take,' said Self-Reliance. 'And the only qualification required was that I spoke well at the interview. I had to take calls all day long and most of the time just had to appease the customer, because there was little else I could do. If we couldn't help them we were told to say the computers were down and could they call back. Most of the calls were to pacify the caller for us not being able to deliver what a particular advertisement offered. People get annoyed at being misled and having their time wasted.'

'When you reach Service City you will learn how the Secret Service follow through on Customer's behalf,' said Intuition. 'These principles may seem ahead of their time but the fact is that they are timeless. With all manners of communication and technology available today, the pace of change seems astounding to us now. But then what we think of as progress, from a contemporary point of view, will be archaic in 100 years. Our descendants will look at our 'revolutionary' and 'state-of-the-art' technology and smile at how unsophisticated it is. That is the nature of technological progress in human civilisation. But the Secrets of Service will always remain the same.'

❏   ❏   ❏

SMITH AND SELF-RELIANCE WERE AMAZED at how busy Superficial Town was. The centre comprised a huge shopping mall with a myriad of businesses all promising something special.

'What an incredible array of merchandise,' said Smith. 'Look how many people are in the shops. I wonder what the service is like?'

'We should keep going straight through,' said Self-Reliance, concerned at the attention they were attracting.

'Hey there! What's your hurry?' said Manipulate. 'I can see that this is your first time here yet you're not interested in looking at what our town has to offer. Why's that, then? I'm sure it's because you don't realise what we have on offer. Come, let me show you.'

Before they could protest Manipulate had led them into a large store. 'In here,' he said to them, 'we have all forms of status on offer. Take your time and look around. You're sure to see something you want.'

Smith watched as all the assistants eyed him expectantly. Several of the younger ones came up to him one after the other asking, 'Can I help you?'

'We're just looking, actually,' said Smith which elicited the reply:

'What is it you're looking for?'

'They must be on commission or something,' said Self-Reliance, 'because they won't leave us alone.'

'And look at the older assistants,' said Smith. 'They seem to be too full of their own importance to pay us any attention at all.'

'Good, while they're not looking let's get out of here, it's so hot and the music is so loud you can hardly hear yourself think,' said Self-Reliance.

'What, leaving already?' said Manipulate who had been watching them. 'Don't tell me there's nothing in here at all for you.'

'Well, we have everything we need at the moment,' replied Smith.

'Need for what?' enquired Manipulate. 'You're on your way to *somewhere* then, I take it?'

Before Self-Reliance could suggest to Smith that it would be better to keep quiet about their destination, Manipulate got it out of him that they were on the way to Prosperity and Service City.

'In that case, we have *lots* that you should be interested in!' said Manipulate. 'You will need a fine frame for the Charter you must be carrying. A fine frame makes it much more meaningful you know. Why, take a look at ours hanging over there. Doesn't it look good?'

Smith was taken over to read it and was shocked at how similar the wording was to his own, though the meaning was clearly different.

'Stand to deliver your money,' it read.

In the meantime, an assistant manager called Plausible took Self-Reliance off in another direction.

'Here, come with me,' Plausible said, 'I've got something to show you and I can assure you that you won't meet with disappointment.'

Then Manipulate looked at Smith and asked if he would show him his charter.

'I stand to deliver service for life' said Smith.

'Then you're in luck,' said Manipulate. 'We've just the position available.'

'But I'm not looking for a position,' protested Smith.

'Of course you are,' said Manipulate, 'everyone wants a good position. And this one has just come up today. Just think of the security in itself. And anyway you don't even know what it is yet. Just wait 'till you hear what it is. Come on, we'll go and visit Prestige at the Status Department. He's always interested in seeing people who are offering something such as you.'

'But I'm not offering anything,' said Smith. 'You're offering me something, which I don't want.'

'Don't *want* the title *Controller* of Service Co-ordination?' said Manipulate. 'Of course you do, and I can see that you're already excited about the prospect. And the good news is that you don't really have to do anything. What more could you want? Now, what else did you want to have? What about membership to our exclusive business club? We're always looking for new blood and with me recommending you, we may even be able to see our way to getting you in as a vice-president or something. What do you think of that, eh? Now, come on, we have the whole Mall to see yet. You don't want to lose out just because someone else beats you to it, you know. Mind you, you should have been here last week.'

'But I wasn't here last week, so what difference would it have made anyway,' said Smith. 'And I would have missed out on the *Controller* position which you say had *just* become available.'

'What sort of an attitude is that?' replied Manipulate, 'I'm just saying you should have been here last week!

107

Still, at least you're here now taking the opportunity to buy.'

'But I'm not buying anything and I don't intend to buy anything either.'

'What do you mean you're not buying anything? You've already committed yourself,' said Manipulate. 'The sign above the entrance door very clearly says that there is a minimum purchase in here.'

'Well, I'm leaving as soon as I've found my companion,' said Smith.

'Oh no you don't! You're not getting out of your obligation to purchase that easily, you know. We have a system to protect us from time wasters like you.'

◻   ◻   ◻

MEANWHILE, UNBEKNOWN TO SMITH, Self-Reliance was being tempted by Plausible to buy a lottery ticket: 'The chances of you winning today are incredible. Just think, one quick purchase and you will be able to make all your dreams come true.'

'I'm already making my dreams come true,' said Self-Reliance, 'everyday of my life I am in command of what I want to be, do and have. And I assure you that I do not want to *have* what you are offering.'

'But how do you really *know* what you want to have until you see it?' argued Plausible. 'We're very experienced in dealing with customers you know and we have found that almost all buy on impulse. And we are proud to satisfy their impulse and, what's more, immediately! Where else would you get such a service? Come on, a little of what you fancy is good for you don't you agree?'

'Yes, so long as whatever it is remains in moderation,' replied Self-Reliance. 'But that is not the point here. You are intent on selling your customers things that you convince them that they need. Whatever you have a surplus of, you make into a good offer. But no matter how good a bargain may be, it is not a bargain if it is not really wanted.'

'So? Who cares? The customer doesn't seem to mind, and we certainly don't, so long as we get a sale. Now are you going to take up this offer or are you wasting my time? If you are we have a system to protect us from people like you.'

□   □   □

SMITH AND SELF-RELIANCE WERE ARRESTED and brought before Judge Find-Fault for examination.

'What do you think you're doing entering our peaceful town and causing a disturbance?' demanded Judge Find-Fault.

'As far as we are aware, we have not caused anything of the sort,' replied Smith. 'Moreover, our intention of passing through quietly was prevented by your townspeople intent on selling to us.'

'And why shouldn't they? It's their town, their wares and therefore their right?' argued Judge Find-Fault. 'I put it to you that the disturbance was caused by you *refusing* to buy, which I might add is a threat to their very livelihood and the existence of our fine town. If this was not the case why did you come here?'

'Because we are on the way to Service City and the only road to it passes through this way,' said Smith.

'And what makes you think for one moment that *it* is worth going to in preference to our fine town? Is it not true that in our market you can get *whatever* you want to have, and *as soon as* you want it?'

'But you have nothing of interest to us,' said Self-Reliance. 'We're journeying towards what we want to *be* and *do*. But here you concentrate on selling to people through peer pressure. But the reality you haven't grasped is that, though people love to buy, they hate to be sold.'

'That sounds very noble, but if the buying decision was left up to the customer no one would ever sell anything! Every shop would incur loss and our town would not exist. I see what you're up to. You've come here to ruin us!' announced Judge Find-Fault. 'My examination of you is concluded and I have decided to send you for trial.'

'Trial?' said Smith, bewildered.

'Yes, you may think that we don't treat people here with any thought, but just to show you that you're *wrong* about us, we will allow you the benefit of a trial,' replied Judge Find-Fault.

'But what are we being charged with?' asked Smith.

'Disturbance of the peace, loitering in the mall, causing unrest among the people and spying,' read Judge Find-Fault from his notes and turning to his clerk Petty said, 'take them down and set the trial for tomorrow.'

'Wait,' said Smith, 'who is going to represent us?'

'The court will take care of that *service* for you,' replied Petty.

□   □   □

THERE WAS LITTLE LIGHT IN THE JAILHOUSE, which was in the basement of the courthouse. Smith and Self-Reliance were put into separate cells that both already held an occupant.

110

'Ah, company at last,' said Smith's cellmate, whose name was Entrepreneur. 'What are you in here for, causing unrest or spying?'

'I take it you that you have been incarcerated under false pretences also then?' replied Smith.

'This town is unbelievable!' said Entrepreneur. 'I have never known anywhere that is so full of people, yet empty of ideas. A cartel of businesses decides what they want to sell and then everyone has to buy into whatever it is, or is considered an outcast of their society. I'm from Prosperity, which to be honest I now wish I had never left. But I was so successful there that I thought it would be a great idea to seek out other markets. This was the first place I came to, but as soon as I started suggesting rewarding customers with things they wanted, but didn't expect, I was accused of causing unrest.'

'But with our trial tomorrow, they seem keen on dealing out their odd sense of justice very quickly here,' said Smith. 'So, how long have you been here? Surely they must have set a trial for you?'

'Well my *trial* has started three times in fact but on each occasion I have come up with an idea that they are not sure whether they like, so they have postponed sentencing me.'

'Sentence you! But how can they do that if your trial is not even finished?' exclaimed Smith in surprise.

'You will soon see that they can do anything they like. And if they think it's going to be difficult then they just create a title, or a position, so that someone can be in charge of it. The trouble is everybody is so busy giving orders, or arranging meetings, that nothing really ever gets done. Apart from the fact that they seem able to put their case against you, complete with witnesses, in double quick time. Do you know who they have defending you yet?'

'No, we don't, though from what you say it may be better to defend ourselves,' said Smith.

'Fine thought, but they won't let you,' answered Entrepreneur. 'They would accuse you of undermining their process and add it to the other charges they have against you. Well, you'll either get Malevolence, though he usually prosecutes if Judge Find-Fault is unable to, as they take in turns to sit on the bench, or Stigma. Though he only attaches himself to your case at the direction of the Judge.'

'Are you saying that Judge Find-Fault prosecutes as well?' asked Smith incredulously. 'And that the prosecutor, Malevolence, is also a Judge?'

'That's right,' said Entrepreneur. 'So you can be sure of having either judgement, or *grudgement*, passed against you.'

'But that's utter injustice!' said Smith.

'Who said life was a fair game? It's up to you how you play it,' replied Entrepreneur. 'Life isn't the way it's supposed to be; it's just the way it is. After all, two thirds of life is spelled lie isn't it? What makes the difference is the *way* you cope with it.'

'Well, I'm not going to live my life as a lie, whatever the demands or accusations against me. They can say what they want but I'll never recognise what they stand for,' said Smith defiantly.

'That's the spirit,' said Entrepreneur. 'Don't let them weaken your commitment, which is what they'll try to do. I have learned that commitment is not about keeping going when it's easy. Anyone can do that. It's about keeping going when its tough, really tough and the odds are all against you. That's commitment.

'Do you know almost every project that I have ever started has attracted ridicule,' he continued. 'It's almost as if people are determined to see my ideas fail and hope to see me fall flat on my face. Yet, I've discovered that despite all the obstacles, each time I've succeeded, those people who laughed, first began to be resentful for what I had created, and then, in due course they started enjoying the benefits themselves. And you know what they say when they do? They say, wasn't I lucky? Yet, when I started living in Service City, people never laughed. Moreover they wanted me to succeed and expected me to grow.'

'You actually lived there!' exclaimed Smith. 'Then what on earth possessed you to come here?'

'Well, I already told you that I was looking for new markets, in fact it was more to apply my knowledge on new markets. So that others would be able to experience the benefits enjoyed at Service City. What I didn't count on was that the people who live here are embittered because they gave up trying to get to Prosperity.'

'So you assumed their motives to be sincere like yours, while they assumed your motives to be ulterior?' said Smith.

'That's about the picture. But it looks like you're in the same frame.'

□   □   □

ON THEIR WAY UP TO THE COURTHOUSE the following morning, Smith related to Self-Reliance what he had learned from Entrepreneur.

'Well, it seems your company was somewhat more stimulating than mine,' said Self-Reliance, 'I had to share my cell with Contempt. He, too, derided the justice of this town. But he didn't stop there. He was disdainful of all justice everywhere. In fact, he poured scorn on everything, no matter what subject we discussed. He mocked me for considering going to Service City. He

113

jeered at me for having a companion like you that got me locked up in a cell. There was nothing he didn't have a gibe against.'

'Did he say why he was there himself?' asked Smith.

'He said that the court kept putting him there because he couldn't keep his comments to himself during sessions.'

'Well, he's right on one thing,' sighed Smith. 'This court we're about to face is not interested in justice. What are we going to do?'

'We must keep our own counsel,' replied Self-Reliance. 'Because, whatever we say they are intent on turning against us.'

'Quiet in the court room!' called the clerk, Petty, impolitely. 'All rise for his honour Judge Find-Fault.'

'Read out the charge and let's get on,' boomed Judge Find-Fault.

'Will the accused stand,' instructed Petty. 'There are six charges, your honour. Both offenders are charged with disturbing the peace. Loitering in the Mall without any intention of buying anything. Not having sufficient funds to purchase a title, having agreed to do so. Causing unrest among the people who were engaged in going about their business. Defaming the good name of our town through slanderous accusations. Finally, spying on behalf of persons intent on bringing our township to an end. There is actually a seventh charge of wasting the court's time currently held in abeyance pending how the defendants plead your honour.'

'And how do you plead?' enquired Judge Find-Fault frowning at the two bewildered defendants in his dock.

Smith spoke up, 'Conscious of not wanting to waste the court's time, would it be in order to ask to see our counsel before pleading?'

Judge Find-Fault looked at a person sitting directly opposite the clerk, Petty, and raised his eyebrows. The man, who was called Stigma, stood up, directed his attention to the dock and addressed himself to Smith and Self-Reliance.

'I have been attached to you for the duration of this case but let me assure you that I have been fully briefed,' said Stigma, he then turned to face the Judge and added, 'I am advising my clients to plead guilty as charged, milord. On behalf of my clients I would like to ask leniency on the basis that, as it is their first time to Superficial Town and being overwhelmed at what was available here for them, they acted without thinking. On the basis that they be allowed to reside in this town, I ask on their behalf if the charges may be dropped.'

Smith could not believe what was being said and was about to shout his protest when Self-Reliance gripped his arm. 'Wait,' he whispered, 'if the only way we are going to get out of here is by escaping, then we may find it easier do so if we are not behind bars.'

'But we must be true to ourselves,' protested Smith quietly.

'But what good will it do to feed the prefabricated argument? It's just what they want so that more charges can be pressed against us. Their aim is to keep us here no matter how they do it. Remember what Intuition advised: To do whatever we were able to do to get through, without compromising our values; and to keep our mind on why we wanted to get through. He didn't advise us to argue as to why they should not keep us.'

'You're right,' agreed Smith, 'and that Stigma, attached to us, will not let allow anyone listen to us.'

❑   ❑   ❑

'IT IS MY CONSIDERED OPINION that we should not consider dropping the charges until we have heard from the witnesses,' said Judge Find-Fault. 'After all, we are in session at the moment so we wouldn't want to waste the opportunity to engage in what we are good at in Superficial Town: judging people. Bring in the first witness.'

As Manipulate entered, he eyed the two he had managed to get into the dock and looked gratified. His evidence confirmed what the court wanted to hear.

'I went out of my way to please one of them,' he said, 'even to the trouble of showing him what we stood for. Yet, he was only interested in telling me what he was about, and belittled our own words. However, I persevered and offered him one of our best posts. Well, to tell the truth, he was very derogative about being a controller. He didn't even appreciate my offer to introduce him into the local community. Well, I could see that there was no pleasing him, and that people were starting to get out of his way and even leave the premises. So, in adherence of the title of Head of Customer Control, I bought him here.'

'May I ask if at any time you felt that the defendant you refer to did not have sufficient funds to purchase what he wanted?' asked Stigma.

'Not at the time but it soon became clear to me afterwards,' replied Manipulate. 'Why else would he waste my time? Furthermore, he knew he had to purchase something because I pointed out the minimum purchase above the door.'

'No further questions,' said Stigma.

The next witness was Plausible who did the same for Self-Reliance that Manipulate had done for Smith. It was clear to the defendants that his deceptive evidence was just what the court expected to hear. Plausible's testimony seemed to remind Judge Find-Fault of his examination of the two and he made a note of it while looking at Smith.

The witness following Plausible was someone whom Smith recognised from the City of Apathy.

'Yes, I've known that defendant for some years now,' said Resentment, pointing at Smith, 'and he's always been a troublemaker. He always took the best parking space at work, just because his car was better than mine. He tried to tell me that it was because he got in earlier than I did, but that wasn't the real reason. He just wanted to rub my nose in it because he had taken the position that was due to me. And that's only because I wasn't there. One week I'm away, then the next I return and he's taken it.'

'So you should have been there the previous week as he was after the best position?' asked Judge Find-Fault.

'You're telling me! Yet, all he could say was that it was nothing to do with me not being there the week before,' said Resentment. 'I left because of him, I'm sure I did. I bet that's why he's here. He's after the position I got here last week.'

As no questions were forthcoming from Stigma, the last witness was called. Smith also recognised as he had met him on the way to House Integrity.

'He categorically refused to help me in any way whatsoever,' said Bureaucrat. 'All that my colleague and I were interested in was to ease his path, and he flatly refused to co-operate. Because of him we were left in a right mess and that wasted a whole night. It was only by sheer luck that we discovered in the morning that we must have been able to free ourselves during the night. And what was he doing out on the road so late? Spying if you ask me! Because, right after he left us, he started snooping around a large building that was close by.'

'Just because one of my clients did not assist you, which I think we all agree he should have done, does not make him a spy does it?' questioned Stigma.

'That's not for me to judge is it?' answered Bureaucrat. 'All I know is what I've told you. But if you gave me the time to get him to fill out some of my forms I'm sure I could tell you much more.'

'Enough!' interrupted Judge Find-Fault, 'I'll be the judge of what we decide. And though it's clear to me what this court will decide, I would like to hear from the defendants, and there are a couple of further points I want to put to them.'

□   □   □

'NOW,' HE ADDED LOOKING AT SMITH, 'yesterday you argued how people like to buy, but not to be sold. Surely you must realise that for business to make a profit it is logical to sell things?'

'Customers buy for their own reasons not businesses' reasons,' answered Smith. 'And there are only *two* reasons that *any* customer buys anything.'

'Oh really?' Enquired Judge Find-Fault sarcastically. 'And what reasons would those be perchance? Good marketing and well-packaged products no doubt. Well, we *already* know that!'

'Actually the reasons are *good feelings* and *right solutions*,' said Smith.

'Good feelings and right solutions?' said Judge Find-Fault. 'That isn't at all logical. If business were to waste its time asking what made the customer feel good, that would mean that the customer would be dictating how even the production lines would be run. No, that would never work! People buy what's available and fortunately in our town we give them a wide choice. We know what people need. They need status, as well as houses, clothes, food, insurance, computers and cars. We even know that our young customers need toys.'

'People don't want to be sold a house,' said Smith. 'They want a home, to enjoy comfort and contentment. They don't want to be sold clothes. They want to feel good about their appearance. They don't want to be sold a computer. They want to feel the benefits that technology can offer. People don't want to be sold *toys*. They want to buy *happy moments* for their children.

'And what about your other reason, right solutions?' said Judge Find-Fault. 'I suppose you're suggesting that business must know how to define what all the problems of its customers are, so that it can provide a solution? What an impossible and ridiculous state of affairs we'd all be in if that were the case?'

'When we have a problem, none of us are looking to buy things,' answered Smith. 'We want to buy solutions to our problem. People don't need *drill bits*, they want *holes*. They don't want to be sold dishwashers or microwaves. They want to solve their problem of not having enough time because of inconvenient chores. People buy mobile phones, because they want instant communication. The problem is the difference between what we have and what we want. It's up to business to serve its customers by asking them two questions. What is their current situation and how they would like it to change? You gain and develop loyalty with customers by giving them what they want and not what you *think* they should want.'

'You are clearly advocating that we should be spending more of our time on our customers, instead of spending it on our products as we currently do,' said Judge Find-Fault.

'Your intent is to keep customers coming back, isn't it?' asked Smith.

'No, our intent is to keep selling to them,' replied Judge Find-Fault.

'Well, if you focus your attention on your customers they *will* come back. But if you continue to concern yourself about just your wares, you will only find that they don't come back. Greater profitability for your town hinges on how it rewards its customers with good feelings and right solutions. Forget about selling. If you concentrate on helping customers to buy what's best for them they will always buy from you.'

'And you think you know what's best for our town do you, after just a short time eh? Forget about selling? You must be more deranged than we thought. Selling is what keeps us here!'

'But you're not listening,' pleaded Smith who had genuinely believed that he had been getting through. 'Concentrating on how you can assist your customers is a much better principle than the practice of thinking how can I make as many sales as possible today. Don't you know that you have to give before you receive? And where can that be more true than in the business arena.'

'Of course I understand that. We always make sure that people give us the money before we part with our goods,' said Judge Find-Fault.

'There's a big difference between selling and helping people to buy, you know,' returned Smith his voice rising in exasperation. 'Having the attitude of "let's take what we have and talk someone into buying it" is nothing short of manipulative. The customer doesn't like it. Alternatively, finding out what the customer wants and matching it with what you have, ordering it, making it specifically, or sending them to where it can be obtained, is what the customer loves to hear!'

'Enough of this insolence!' shouted Judge Find-Fault. 'I denounce your arguments and find you guilty as charged on all counts. Furthermore, I am not prepared to grant any leniencies because of the mitigation that Stigma attached to your case. You are too dangerous to live in Superficial because you undermine our way of life. Now what is to be done with you?'

'It has been said that you keep people who don't conform to Superficial Town life incarcerated' said Self-Reliance. 'But to my mind my companion will still be able to influence your people. Might I suggest to your honour that we be put to death? But *please* do not banish us from your town for that would be unbearable.'

'Hmmm, I like what you suggest, but why should I not banish you both and be done with it?' replied Judge Find-Fault.

'Banishment for us would be a fate worse than death because we would be tarnished with the reputation of having been refused Superficial life. We would have to put up with people's taunts about how stupid we were to give up the opportunity of having whatever status or possession we wanted immediately.'

'Your argument is strong, but once again I refuse you leniency,' said Judge Find-Fault. 'My judgement is that you will be taken from this court immediately and forcibly *banished* from our town. And your name will be placed on posters that we will place around the town as a reminder of how *we* in Superficial remain *uninfluenced* by your ideas.'

◻   ◻   ◻

AND SO IT WAS THAT SMITH AND SELF-RELIANCE could quit the deluded streets and hypocritical shops of the town that would not listen. As they were taken to the town

121

limits, posters were being put up proclaiming: 'Superficial is no place for Self-Reliance, or those that choose to travel with him.'

'That was brilliant of you to confidently propose what you did,' said Smith when they were safe beyond the town's borders. 'I'm afraid I got so wound up with the whole attitude of the court that I couldn't stop myself from preaching but I really thought that they were taking on board what I was saying.'

'Your arguments were both principled and well founded but the harder you pushed them the further your listeners went away from you,' said Self-Reliance. 'I could see that the Judge was only interested in finding fault in your arguments. That's all he was looking for, so it would not have mattered what you had said.'

'That's why you requested the death penalty for us, of course. I couldn't believe my ears when I heard you!'

Self-Reliance laughed. 'Because he took the opposite approach to everything by pleading my case for destroying us, which was the course he favoured, he was forced to take the alternative. It was the best choice for his town, as far as he could see.'

'But why could he not see what I was getting at?' asked Smith.

'Because, like Entrepreneur, you were trying to get him to buy into your ideas by saying things he just didn't want to hear. He believed that your ideas would make the people, his customers, more important than he was. As leader of this town he likes the way it is and sees no reason to have it any other way. He has made all of the townspeople as judgmental as him because it is a practice that has worked so well for him, he now considers it to be a principle worth fighting for.'

'Yes, I could see that he was unable to recognise the difference between the Principle of Service and the practice of selling,' said Smith.

'Few recognise that there are major differences between principles and practices,' said Self-Reliance. 'Where man-made practices, rules and conventions may differ between the City of Apathy and Service City, for instance, the principle of fire will burn in both cities with the same ferocity. Man does not invent Principles and they apply in all situations whatever the circumstances. But because Man invents practices, whenever he experiences a difficulty he looks for his security in a practice. But often what happens is that as time goes by people believe the practice is a principle that must be followed. Whereas of course the circumstance may no longer be appropriate.'

'So where Judge Find-Fault believes he is sticking to Principles, he is really only applying Superficial practices,' said Smith. 'No wonder he was not prepared even to listen to me, because I threatened what he sees as his guiding principles?'

'Absolutely! The laws that Judge Find-Fault invented to suit Superficial Town have now been around for so long that I suppose he is unaware of what real guiding principles are. His selling practices have become the misguided principles that guide all of his decisions.

'Which is why our presence threatened him. When we live our lives based on principles; we can apply them in any circumstance. Applying a practice may address a current problem, but understanding the principle behind the practices allows us to meet future challenges actively.'

'Most principles are common sense, of course, like listening before speaking, starting at the beginning, and sowing before reaping, said Self-Reliance. 'Yet, there is paradox to following principles. For example, when you give up trying to impress a group, you become more impressive; or a show of strength suggests insecurity, which is certainly what Judge Find-Fault and his colleagues suffered from.'

'The less you make of yourself, the more you become. I just wish I had realised this before the court case,' said Smith

'But it was your actions that brought about my insight to propose what I did. You stuck to what you believed in and it was the values of integrity, fairness, sincerity and discipline you displayed, that the Superficial people disliked. Values that are guided by those Principles which are essential in developing excellence and depth of character.'

'I just wish I could have got them to see the power of the Principle of Service,' said Smith.

'That is, to always serve others in a way that you would wish to be served, for your return will always equal your service.'

'Yes, we develop ourselves best through others,' added Self-Reliance.

'You know, I believe that business is like playing tennis.'

'In what way?' asked Smith. 'Well, those who don't learn to serve well, always end up losing!'

<<< AGENT SMITH FILE NOTE >>>

1. Have the courage of your convictions.

2. Resolve to follow through what you start.

3. Customer loyalty is built on delivery, not promise.

4. Marketing is building relationships, not a sales tool.

5. Good feelings and right solutions are why customers buy.

6. The little things build a competent, trustworthy reputation.

7. Stay committed when the going gets really tough.

8. Apply Principles of Service in preference to selling practices.

9. When you stop trying to impress you become more impressive.

006

Trapped at Hesitation Castle

WITH SUPERFICIAL TOWN BEHIND THEM, Smith and Self-Reliance could once more see their way ahead. The road was straight though narrower; its surface strewn with sharp rocks that they had to pick their way through.

'Wait for us!' shouted a voice behind and turning they made out two figures coming towards them.

'They must be from Superficial Town,' said Smith, as he eyed the buildings in the distance warily. 'Why do you think they are chasing us?'

'We'll soon find out,' said Self-Reliance, as the two caught up.

'You must be twins,' said Smith.

'You're not the first to say so. In fact we bear no relation to each other at all. I am Spontaneity and this is Impulsiveness. When I heard that Judge Find-Fault had banished you, which is something he has never done before, the timing was perfect for me. I was already taking voluntary action to leave Superficial.'

'And those banishment posters spurred me to action,' put in Impulsiveness. 'When I saw my neighbour here take off, I didn't waste any time reflecting, I just joined up with him.'

'I wasn't intending to follow you,' said Spontaneity. 'But would like to go with you to Prosperity.'

'Well, I'm here because of you, make no mistake,' said Impulsiveness. 'The rumours about your service principles sound like just the thing I want to be part of.'

126

'I'm glad to hear that some people took notice,' said Smith.

Spontaneity looked sad, 'Not everyone wants to be in Superficial. It's just that the majority of Superficial people have been acquiescent and obsequious when faced with authority and it has become a way of life.'

'It amazes me,' added Self-Reliance, 'that most people continue to give up their individuality to be like others.'

'Fulfilling our potential' said Spontaneity, 'and being the person we are destined to be, will only come when we follow our true nature. To worry and fret about trivial things such as wearing the *right* clothes, living in the *right* house and driving the *right* car, is to cocoon ourselves within the culture of what other people consider is best for us.'

'Where are you from originally?' asked Smith.

'I was born in Frankness, not far from here, in fact. When I was young I took the Freedom Road intending to go straight to Prosperity. I stopped in Superficial, thinking I had already made it there. I didn't realise that I had been lulled into a false sense of security. I involved myself in my work - it was well paid with the promise of a good pension - and I managed to buy a property in the most prestigious area of the town, Deluded Hollow.

'Then, this morning I woke up and was suddenly struck by the mistake I was making. I hadn't contented myself. I had contained myself. I wasn't doing what I wanted to do, or living where I wanted to be. I was enjoying a comfortable existence, but I wasn't fulfilling myself. I was so busy chasing my pension I had forgotten my passion. I wanted to feel passionate again about what I did and how I lived. I did not want my epitaph to read: Died at thirty, buried at eighty. So, I immediately decided that the next fifty years would be spent fulfilling my potential, which is why I am once more on my way to Prosperity!'

'This Prosperity place sounds just the place for me, too!' said Impulsiveness excitedly. 'I lived in Superficial for as long as I can remember but I've always been restless there. But you'll be glad that I have joined you because I know this part of the road that we're on like the back of my hand and you'll be pleased to learn that just ahead of us now there is Short-cut Meadow. Look, there it is now, come on!'

'I don't think we should divert from our road, even though walking on these sharp rocks is hard work,' said Self-Reliance cautiously.

Smith, whose feet were beginning to hurt, looked at the short-cut.

'You see!' shouted Impulsiveness. 'Look how that path doesn't divert from ours at all. It follows alongside.'

Smith looked at Self-Reliance. 'So long as it does run parallel, let's take the opportunity to walk on the easier path. If it starts to go off in a different direction we can easily get back again.'

Self-Reliance stepped over the stile and looked at the softer path before him. It certainly looked more pleasant and it did run alongside.

'OK, but only as far as it goes our way,' said Self-Reliance.

As each of the four travellers stepped over the stile in turn they all failed to notice the broken sign that lay hidden in the hedge. Unwittingly, they had stepped directly into the State of Limbo.

□   □   □

THEY HAD BEEN WALKING AND TALKING for sometime when Self-Reliance noticed that the hedge to the side of them had become really thick. It was so thick that it was not possible to see their former road on the other side.

'I think we'd better find a way through here or go back before we get lost,' he said to the others. 'And it will be getting dark soon.'

'Well, it seems a long way to have to go back,' said Smith feeling guilty. 'Perhaps there will be a way through any minute. Let's keep an eye out for a place where we can squeeze through.'

'Or ask someone for directions, what about that man over there,' suggested Spontaneity, pointing towards another traveller resting on the side of the bank just ahead of them.

'Excellent idea!' agreed Smith approaching the stranger. 'Hi! I see that you're going in the same direction as us. Do you know where this road leads? Does it join back up the one that runs alongside?'

'It is said that this road leads to Prosperity,' said Rationale. 'As for joining up with the other road I can only say that it would be reasonable for it to do so, wouldn't you?'

'There, I told you so!' exclaimed Impulsiveness.

'Would you happen to know how much farther it is?' asked Smith. 'With daylight fading it would be good to reach it before nightfall.'

'I don't see why you shouldn't,' answered Rationale. 'But then I don't see why you should either. There should be an inn, or guesthouse, just a little further on. It's better to stay there and arrive at Prosperity during the day, isn't it? Perhaps you could ask them to keep a room for me if you find one. I'm sure that they wouldn't mind doing so, would they? I'm just going to rest here a little longer as I have only just stopped. There would be no sense in going on immediately after I've just stopped, would there now?'

'Well, we could rest here with you for a while, and then we could go on together,' proposed Smith.

'What would be the sense in that?' replied Rationale. 'You weren't going to stop and don't need a rest. You only stopped because you were unsure of where you were heading. No, it makes sense that you go ahead doesn't it?'

Feeling rather confused Smith joined his three companions and they continued in the growing darkness.

'Listening to him didn't give me any confidence at all,' said Self-Reliance.

'No, but it does make more sense to go on rather than go back,' said Smith. 'And anyway there's bound to be something up ahead isn't there? It stands to reason, doesn't it? Why would there not be a guesthouse on the road to Prosperity for weary travellers?'

'If we're not sure whether we're on the right road the only sensible thing to do is to go back, regardless of how much we have to retrace our steps,' commented Self-Reliance. 'It's probably because you *want* this to be the right road so much that you are already talking like that stranger back there.'

□　　　　□　　　　□

AS NONE OF THE FOUR TRAVELLERS felt inclined to say anything to each other, they travelled in silence while it grew darker. Each of their minds was occupied with their own thoughts, not least Smith who had been stung by Self-Reliance's comments. 'It was true,' he thought, 'I *do* want this to be the right road and, because of it, I am already convincing myself that there is good reason for taking it. But how do I know for certain? Intuition was precise in his guidance not to leave the straight path after leaving Superficial, despite how difficult it might become. And at the first opportunity what do I do? I take the easiest route that is offered. But that stranger did say that this would lead to Prosperity. Why would he say that if it were not the case? What would he gain by advising people wrongly? And he said that there must be a place to rest shortly, didn't he? Well, why would he say that if there weren't? Hmm, perhaps Self-Reliance is right. I'm even beginning to think like that stranger. How strange it is that people can contract doubts and fears from one another like illnesses.'

'Look, there is a light up ahead of us, See!' Impulsiveness' shout brought Smith back instantly from his reverie.

Following the direction of the light, they soon came upon an enormous building that, in the dark, looked derelict and uninviting.

'It's just like some fortress,' said Spontaneity. 'Look at the turrets. For a guesthouse, it's certainly more foreboding than welcoming.'

As the four of them pondered whether to knock on the large entrance door or not, they was a rumble of thunder and it began to rain.

'It's no good vacillating is it,' said Smith feeling as guilty of it as the others. 'We're going to get completely soaked if we stay here. Let's knock and ask if they can put us up for the night. Even if they can't help us at least they'll be able to provide us with some temporary shelter, can't they?'

Knocking on the door made an empty echoing sound. A few moments later the door opened and there stood before them a giant of a man. He was so large that he completely filled the doorway blocking out the light that was behind him.

'Good evening,' started Smith, 'Sorry to disturb you, but we're looking for a guesthouse we were told would be near here. We were wondering if this was it?'

The giant man looked at them solemnly with dark brooding eyes.

'It was, once,' he growled in a low voice, 'in happier times that is. Before they changed the state boundary. Travellers are few now, mores the pity.'

With a loud crack of lighting and an almost instantaneous clap of thunder, the heavens opened and the rain poured down.

'Can we shelter anyway, at least until the rain stopped?' requested Smith.

The gigantic man's eyes seem to bore right through the four of them huddled around his doorway. The next moment, he stepped back and pulled the door wide open, let them in then turned the lock and pocketed the key.

'Follow me,' he growled and led the way down the corridor to a large reception hall. Smith could see that in earlier days this had been an elegant room. But the heavy drapes that hung around it were now jaded, worn and dusty. There was dust everywhere. The backs of the large wing chairs that faced the fireplace, the tables, the picture and the bookcases were all in need of a clean. One of the tables looked as though it had been hewn out of stone. On its surface rested a large book that had clearly not been opened for a very lengthy period.

'No one's touched this place for years,' whispered Self-Reliance to Smith.

'Let's have your passes then,' boomed their enormous host. 'I shouldn't have let you in without them.'

Smith looked at the bewildered faces staring at him.

'We're not certain what you mean by passes,' said Smith.

'Your passes! Everybody must have a pass. It's the law! It's not my fault that they changed the boundary. But it's more than my job's worth not to see your passes. Come on!' he growled.

'I've lost mine tonight,' Impulsiveness lied. 'But I'm sure I'll find it tomorrow when it's light.'

'That's no excuse! It's hardly my fault that you've gone and been careless, is it? There's no way I'm going to have condemnation against me just because of your neglect in looking after your pass. Everyone knows that here in the State of Limbo it's against the law to do anything without a pass.'

The giant's eyes glared at them. 'So that's why you tricked me into letting you in, just so that you could get me into trouble! Well it's unfair to put me in a position where I can be accused of not doing what I'm meant to be doing. Stay here and don't move!'

The four men stood there stunned as the large man stormed out of the room. 'I can't believe what's happening here,' said Smith. 'And what are we doing in the State of Limbo, of all places? Is this a guesthouse or not? And who is this person who seems intent on calling others to count for everything?'

◻   ◻   ◻

'HESITATION CASTLE IS WHERE YOU ARE and Giant Blame is your host,' said a voice from behind one of the large winged chairs.

'And, yes, you are in the sorry State of Limbo, which you must have entered illegally, otherwise you would have a pass,' said a second voice from behind another chair.

The two people who had spoken got out of their chairs and came forward to introduce themselves. The

133

one who had spoken first was Attentive. She explained how she had followed a request from the State to help with improving communication lines to neighbouring provinces. She had been sent a pass and had stopped off at Hesitation Castle because it was the nearest place to the border shared with Good Fortune.

The other was named Indignant, who did actually reside in the Limbo and did have a pass, but unfortunately *had* lost it that day. He was livid that Giant Blame had taken him to task so much for what was surely a common error and even more angry because the 'oaf,' as he had put it, would not let him go until he showed him his pass.

'And how can I show him something I haven't got?' said Indignant. 'It really is too bad! And what's worse is that I have to pay for my room as long as I stay here, even though the oaf insists on keeping me here! He keeps on about it not being his fault and that they should never have changed the state line. Absolute poppycock, that's what I say!'

'But what does he mean by that?' asked Smith. 'It's almost the first thing he said to us. He appears to be very annoyed about whatever it is.'

'Well, a long time ago Hesitation Castle was actually the entrance to Good Fortune,' began Attentive.

'We're that close!' interrupted Smith.

'Well, you were that close but, since the change, this castle now lies on a different path,' replied Attentive.

'Why was the state line changed?' asked Self-Reliance.

'Now, there's a story,' she began. 'Legend holds that this castle used to be a fine place where enthusiastic travellers on their way to Prosperity would enjoy a very brief sojourn before finally coming into Good Fortune. For those committed to leaving their State of Mediocrity it was like an oasis of thankful refreshment. It offered a precursor of the lifestyle, they would experience if they stayed firm to their resolve. It was more a passing out academy, than anything else I suppose. Its motto was: *He who hesitates is lost*, adhering to the philosophy that the individual who knows what they stand for, follows their heart and is able to align what they do with what they are, will *never* hesitate.

'Now you may have noticed that this academy is built like a fortress. And the reason for that was very simple. Those who were on their way to reaching Prosperity understood that there were two further elements that were required to harness all the key attributes of an individual for continuous and successful growth. These were leadership and teamwork. And only those who were able to work together towards a shared purpose were able to find their way out of the fortress, enter Good Fortune and go forward to Prosperity. Those who were unable to work with like-minded people and who did not act with the attributes of a leader when under pressure would reveal their doubts about what to do. Their hesitation therefore would be their downfall.

'Things started to go wrong, however, when some people reached here that were unsure of their motives, did not know what they stood for and had no idea about aligning their personal mission with their professional one. But they still wanted the benefits that Good Fortune offered. Unfortunately their numbers grew into an unwelcome force that would not leave. Wanting the benefits of success without paying the price in advance, they misused the advantages that were available here and created anarchy. So Prosperity altered the boundary.

'It was a simple thing to do' continued Attentive, 'because they saw the real success in reaching Prosperity was more of a journey than actually a destination. So they gave this part of the land of Good Fortune to the State of Limbo for those people who wanted to periodically enjoy a part of it, but were unable to get to Prosperity. The road was then littered with obstacles with a view to building leadership and teamwork attributes for dedicated aspiring agents.

'Well, you can imagine how absolutely delighted the misguided travellers were with themselves. But, as they had done nothing to deserve it, what they had achieved did not hold value for them. Even though they convinced themselves that they had finally got just what they really wanted, they allowed this great building to fall into disrepair.

'As for Giant Blame, he was one of the original operatives who blamed Prosperity for making entry too difficult for certain people. Convinced he was being penalised he chose to stay here. He wasn't always a giant but after countless years of negative feelings that the world was out to get him, and never letting go of the resentment that built up within him, he just grew and grew. Unfortunately, though, he remained small-minded, never accepting that it is up to the individual to make a contribution in life and not the other way around.

'I don't know whether what they say is true or not, but the fact is that he seems unable to leave here now. He continually thinks about how things could have been for him and doesn't say much, apart from how unfair it is that such things did not transpire. Of course, with his job of checking the passes that the State of Limbo insists you carry, he has found a purpose in line with the temperament he has grown. And why the 'passes' you may want to know? They are simply to indicate to the State that you *know* your place. Anyone not carrying such a pass will be considered a threat, because without one they must be holding aspirations above their station, and must be considering leaving Limbo.'

'Well, I have no such aspiration!' Indignant said. 'I'm very happy with my place here and its an absolute outrage that this oaf is preventing me from staying here of my own free will!'

'Don't you mean *leaving* here of your own free will,' offered Spontaneity.

'I'm quite aware of what I mean, thank you very much, and the last thing I need is another busybody telling what I mean or don't mean'. With that Indignant left the room mumbling something about making someone pay under his breath.

□   □   □

SMITH FELT DOWNHEARTED. To hear that he had been so close to Good Fortune and had once more taken himself off the right path hit him hard. Worse than that, he had ignored Self-Reliance's caution and led his companion into the same predicament. Still, the fact was that he was here and he must now concentrate on what he must do next and not dwell on past mistakes. That's what he had learned: Never look backwards with blame, when you can move forward with solutions.

'Well we have aspirations to get out,' he said to Attentive while glancing at Self-Reliance. 'Any suggestions on how we can?'

'Getting out is not going to be easy. I'm sure you noticed that Giant Blame pocketed the key for the door when you came in,' answered Attentive. 'Furthermore, this place is a fortress, most of the windows have bars, and those that don't are too narrow to pass through.'

'There must be other entrances,' Self-Reliance put in. 'How about the ways that those agents working in teams left by?'

'Giant Blame has blocked up the ones he knew of, but can't have found them all.'

'Then we must find one of those,' said Smith defiantly.

'It's your best course of action, for you definitely must get out. There is no way that Giant Blame will let you go without a pass. He is able to provide you with one himself, but not until at least one year has passed,' said Attentive flatly.

'One year!' cried Impulsiveness. 'What does he expect us to do meantime?'

'Quite simply he expects you to be his paying guests which, even if you have to stay here a couple of days, is no holiday, I assure you. The lady of the house is called Taunt and though she is supposedly your hostess, there is no pleasing her. But you will soon learn this since the serving of dinner is imminent.'

'At least we're being fed,' said Smith looking on the positive side. 'Any idea how we should go about finding one of the old escape routes?'

'No, I can't help you there. The only thing that may help though is that agents were advised to lead their way to freedom and fortune as a team.' At that moment a loud dinner gong sounded. 'Ah,' added Attentive, 'dinner is about to be served. Come on.'

'But Giant Blame told us to stay here,' said Impulsiveness.

'Only so he can reproach you later. But as he will still charge you for dinner even if you don't eat it, you'd better come along. It's a no win house he runs here you know.' Attentive raised her eyebrows. 'Improving communication lines? I've certainly got my work cut out in the State they're in, haven't I?'

□   □   □

'YOU WOULD HAVE THOUGHT that they would at least clean the place,' commented Smith as he walked the long corridor that led from the reception hall to the dining room. 'With a bit of effort it would look fantastic.'

'Yes, it must have done when the people that ran it did so because they wanted to,' answered Self-Reliance. 'People perform the best and deliver the best service when they like what they do. Our hosts certainly detest what they do, but are determined to hang on to what they have.'

Dinner was an experience that Smith would never forget. He could see that Indignant had been seated in the corner and was sharing a table with another diner called Irritable. Indignant was not happy about having to share and, between exchanging heated words with his fellow diner, was vigorously trying to attract the attention of one of the two people serving. One of these was called Lazy and the other Slow. Neither of them appeared to know what they were doing.

'It's no good skulking over there you know!' bellowed a voice and turning towards it Smith saw a large woman with a scornful face beckoning them.

'That must be Taunt,' said Impulsiveness. 'We'd better do what she says.'

Smith could see that Attentive had already gone straight to a table and started to follow her.

'You'll sit where you're told to, young man,' shrieked Taunt. 'How many of you are there anyway?'

'There are four of us but we would like to sit with that lady over there,' Smith answered pointing towards Attentive. 'Have you a table for five please.'

'Five! Five! Who do you think you are?' scoffed Taunt. 'Whoever heard of five sitting together? Can't you see that all the tables are laid out to fours, twos and ones? There isn't a table for five!'

'That table of six over there would be fine,' offered Smith.

'But there aren't *six* of you are there? No. I'll tell you where you can sit. I can see *you* must be the visitors without passes. This is *my* domain and you ought to count yourself lucky for eating here.'

The four companions were seated at a table and after five minutes were asked by Slow what they wanted. Upon hearing that they had not yet chosen because they did not what was available, Slow went over to Lazy who a few minutes later returned with a menu.

When Slow came back after what seemed an eternity the four learned that the choices were not available, but they could have the roast.

Slow and Lazy delivered the meals, at different times, and unfortunately, did not return with clean cutlery until the meal was cold. This was not difficult because the food had been served on cold plates.

Such a travesty of dining continued throughout the meal until Giant Blame showed them to their rooms, where they were at last allowed to freshen up, after they had paid for their dinner and board.

□   □   □

EACH OF THEIR GUESTROOMS HAD NAMES instead of numbers. Smith and Self-Reliance were given the room named *Leadership*; and Spontaneity and Impulsiveness were shown into a room called *Team-Building*. Because it was the biggest the four agreed to meet in *Team-Building* Room, in order to discuss their escape. First they took the opportunity to freshen up.

As Smith was waiting for Self-Reliance, he looked at the numerous pictures that hung around the walls. The first one was of a man entering into a large building leading three others behind him.

The words inscribed were:

*Leadership is a commonplace activity that can be
developed in ourselves, yet in looking for that
which we expect to see we do not always realise this.
It is a transaction entered into and maintained voluntarily
based on mutual trust, respect and communication.*

The second picture showed two men, but they were one and the same.

One appeared to be following the other while the second was gazing directly out of the picture with eyes that seemed to look at Smith regardless of where he stood to the front or either side of the picture.

The inscription read:

*Do not expect to lead others before you can direct yourself,
for the best leaders are followers of truth. People become their
own leaders when they are in command of themselves.
You will become your own leader
when you become true to yourself.*

The third picture was of a man pulling a chain through water, with the words:

*Like water, true leaders are yielding knowing that
their followers do so without resistance or pressure.*

*Leaders do not push, they pull through example knowing
that you don't push chain links for direction,
you pull them for alignment.
In this way leaders recognise the weak link
that impedes the strength of the whole chain.*

Smith crossed the room to look at the fourth picture. It was of a man holding a set of balance scales while looking through a window. The inscription read:

*Knowing that it is not possible to look through a
window that has only been cleaned on one side,
the true leader will neither attack nor defend,
but will weigh both sides of any situation.
a leader pays equal attention to all disputes
and is aware of prejudices in judgement.*

A fifth picture was of man walking through a wall to a magical land beyond. In one hand he carried a scroll, in the other a bag of gold. The inscription read:

*There is nothing that can withstand the
true leader whose deeds match his words.
Such a person does not lead for the sake of money
or praise yet receives both in abundance.
The true leader communicates the vision of the way
forward that leads to fortune and freedom.*

'You know these pictures are really unusual,' said Smith to Self-Reliance. 'They give sound advice, but they do *more* than that. There is something about them that is compelling. Here, come and take a look.'

Self-Reliance began to read each inscription as Smith had done. 'Well, they are words of wisdom, but then this room *is* called *Leadership* so they probably just follow the room's theme. It's the same man in every picture, though the context of the picture is unusual.'

Smith looked again at the last picture of the set. 'But look at the last words over here: *"the way forward that leads to fortune and freedom."* Isn't that exactly what we want? Once we escape from Hesitation Castle we can enter the Good Fortune! I believe that the pictures are revealing a way out of here.'

'Well, I can't solve them now,' replied Self-Reliance. 'Come on, let's go and meet with the others. They may have similar pictures.'

◻   ◻   ◻

IN *TEAM-BUILDING* ROOM, SPONTANEITY had also been looking at the room's pictures, certain they were hiding some message. The first picture was the world, split into four parts. In the centre was a man holding a scroll in one hand and a broken chain link in the other. The inscription read:

When his world is fragmented,
what is the value of man's law?
In wholeness the parts are greater,
for together everyone achieves more.
Agreement of agenda is in the hands of all,
though the weakness of one will make harmony fall.

The second picture depicted two scenes. The first was of the same man struggling to push a stone. On top of the stone lay a closed book. To the side of him stood three other men that appeared to be indifferent to his struggles. The second scene showed the book, now open, and the four people holding the stone above their heads with ease. The inscription read:

When communication is shut, what strength has a man?
Such weakness will never fulfil a plan.
When open and clear a man is stronger than a fort,
for nothing can resist him when there is willing support.

The third and final picture depicted the same four people as the previous scene. All of them were sitting in a circle. But they neither sat on seats, for there were none, nor on the floor. Each person was supported on the knees of the person behind him. Upon each of their heads they wore a crown of laurel leaves. In the centre of their circle was a gold cup with four handles that each member of the circle held. The inscription read:

With shared objectives respite is always
near and heavy work becomes light.
Against such unified purpose there can be little fight.
When mutual recognition and respect to each is served,
the rewards for endeavour are justly deserved.

Having tried to interest Impulsiveness in the pictures, Spontaneity was pleased to see Smith immediately read the inscriptions.

'This is hardly the time to become art critics,' Impulsiveness said restlessly. 'How are we going to get back home, that's what I want to know?'

'Look,' said Smith to Self-Reliance, beckoning him towards the pictures. 'These three have the same cryptic scenes as the one in our room. I'm sure that they contain some answer to how we can escape.'

'The same man appears in these pictures as in our room, but again they're probably just here because they go with the room's theme,' Self-Reliance replied.

'But think about what Attentive told us,' said Smith. 'That agents could lead their way out as a team to *freedom* and *fortune*. Well we're going to Good *Fortune* when we escape from here, aren't we!'

Smith made a mental note to stop sounding like the stranger that had directed them. 'Every thing I say I am rationalising,' he thought. 'I must be more confident when I speak, I am sounding doubtful.'

'And those words in one of our rooms' pictures said the same thing,' put in Self-Reliance.

'Then let's study all the pictures in both of our rooms, and work over them together. That way, if there is some meaning to them, we can decipher it!' said Spontaneity.

'Well, don't count me in,' Impulsiveness said impetuously. 'I'm exhausted so I'm going to sleep. I'd be at home now if you hadn't influenced me.'

'Look here,' said Smith as he began to re-read the first picture. 'These words tell us "*together everyone achieves more.*" If you take the first letters of each word, you spell TEAM! Come on, this is no time to be tired. We must work together.'

'Well I don't want to!' shouted Impulsiveness, while turning over on the bed he had been lying on. 'You got us into this mess with all your conflicting ideas in Superficial Town. So, as far as I'm concerned, it's up to you to get us out of here.'

Smith wanted to argue that it had been nothing to do with him that Impulsiveness had followed him. Moreover, it was the man's own recommendation that they took the road that they did. But he stopped himself from reacting. This is not the way a true leader would act, he thought: a leader wouldn't react. If that first picture were true, he realised, and leadership was within him, then he must act as though it were. 'And how can I expect him to want to follow me if I do not sound certain of myself? That second picture said that a leader must be in command of himself.

If I am to lead everyone *out* of here, where they have followed me, then I must build their belief in me, not their doubt in me. But what was it that other picture said. *"Recognise the weak link that impedes the strength of the whole."* I must be careful that I do not allow this person's doubts to permeate us all. Or, is it my own uncertainty? Why should I think that I could lead the others? Self-Reliance is most assuredly his own man and Spontaneity has a creative strength that any leader would be proud to have. Let it be their choice to decide who is leader. For now I must lead myself by following my heart. And my heart tells me I must discourage any unrest.'

Going over to Impulsiveness, he said, 'Whatever your reasons were for leaving Superficial Town, it means a great deal that you took the action you did in following me. For I know that you put yourself at risk of being mocked by Superficial people. And I appreciate that when our feet were aching you were enthusiastic in your suggestion for us to take an easier route. I accept full responsibility for us actually taking it and indeed for leading everyone here into the predicament we are now in. Yet, even though we are all tired, I sincerely believe that it is unwise for us to do nothing and just wait for some uncertain fate.

'We must take action ourselves and we must do so now. In this way, we will dispel our doubts and be the master of our own destiny. When we get out of here I promise that we will go straight back to the turnstile where we turned off our former path. At that point you will be able to choose which way you want to go. Should you choose to return, you can blame me for leading you out of the town. Should you decide to continue with us, you will be more than welcome. But right now I need your help. We all need your help. And though I don't yet know the full significance of these pictures, look at what the third in your room says. It advises that *"with shared objectives respite is always near and heavy work becomes light."* Well, we all share a common objective. To leave this place before the service kills us! Come on, with your valued input we will be able to decipher the full significance that is hidden from us.'

At this, Impulsiveness nodded, got up and went straight towards the first picture. 'Come on all of you,' he said, 'let's get on with it.'

The atmosphere that had a few moments before weighed heavy in the room was now instantly transformed into a more light-hearted one. Both Self-Reliance and Spontaneity regarded Smith with genuine respect and admiration.

□   □   □

DURING THE NIGHT, THE FOUR STUDIED the notes that they had independently made from observing all eight pictures from the *Leadership* and *Team-Building* rooms.

'It strikes me that the pictures reveal first and foremost the importance of leadership attributes in developing a strong team. But there must be a second meaning to the pictures,' offered Smith.

'It's as though the chain, window, scales, scroll and gold are symbols for something,' added Impulsive.

'Well, the man that leads everyone into the building in picture one is the same man that walks through a wall in picture five. I believe that the building is this castle and that the wall that appears solid is actually a way out, though that probably doesn't make much sense,' said Spontaneity.

'The second *Team-Building* picture refers to a fort,' said Smith. 'Do you remember how Attentive referred to this place as being a fortress? Well, somehow by putting together all our strength we become stronger than the fort, because it cannot contain us. Perhaps the stone that can't be pushed by the one man is to be lifted by us all. That could be the wall we pass through.'

'But how could we all pass through with a stone above our heads unless something held it there, assuming there is a wall or stone that must be moved?' asked Impulsiveness.

'Perhaps a chain is pulled to lift it!' said Spontaneity. 'One picture shows pushing does not work and another says *"don't push chain links for direction, pull them for alignment."'*

'It will be dawn soon,' said Smith. 'I propose that we actually explore as much as we can to see if anything we come across bears any resemblance to the symbols in the pictures.'

'But the light is not that good to see yet and not only that this castle is enormous. We could easily get lost,' said Impulsiveness.

'It would be better if we could find a plan,' suggested Self-Reliance. 'Perhaps Attentive would know if one exists.'

'A plan! Of course,' said Smith. '*When communication is shut, such weakness will never fulfil a plan,*" are among the words inscribed. 'There must be a plan of this fortress in a book and I know where! Come on we won't get lost just going back to Reception Hall.'

Making their way quietly past the dining room, through the corridor and back to the Reception Hall was easier than they imagined, as a few lights had been left on. Upon entering the hall, Smith headed straight for the large stone table he had noticed upon his arrival. The book that lay on it was covered in dust.

'See a closed book upon a stone,' whispered Smith. 'You can't get much closer to the picture than that.' Opening it carefully Smith could see that it was like a large encyclopaedia.

'Look for a map or plan of the place,' suggested Impulsiveness. 'There must be something that will help us.'

Smith looked under P for plan, M for map, and C for communication without luck.

'It doesn't look as though what we expected to see is here,' said Impulsiveness.

'What did you say?' asked Smith. 'Those words ring a bell. Someone read out from our notes.'

'This is it,' said Self-Reliance. *'Leadership is a commonplace activity in ourselves, but in looking for that which we expect to see we do not always realise this.* Look under L.'

Smith quickly turned to L but again nothing was forthcoming. 'Hey, it's telling us to look for leadership in ourselves. That means O.' Smith turned to O and immediately saw a huge circle filling the page. At the top of the circle there was a flame. Just in front of the flame there were steps. To the right side of the circle was a stone. 'This must be it!' said Smith.

'But it doesn't even look like a map, let alone the plan of a fortress we're in,' said Impulsiveness as he waved his hands around the room. 'Hang on; look at this room we're in. It's almost a perfect circle, isn't it?'

'And that flame must be indicating the position of the fireplace which is at the top of the room,' put in Self-Reliance.

'In which case there must be a hidden doorway, but there's no stone where it should be,' said Spontaneity.

'This must be the stone! It's just in the wrong place,' said Smith and he started to push it.'

'Such weakness will never fulfil a plan,' said Spontaneity. 'We have to do it together.' Though the four tried to push, the stone table was too heavy to budge.

'It's not working,' said Smith breathlessly. 'We must be not doing it right. There must be a way of lifting it. After all didn't one of the pictures show the stone above their heads? One of us stand guard, we'll put on the lights on so that we can see better what we're doing.'

With the light full on a series of pictures above the fireplace became visible. 'Look at those pictures above the fireplace,' said Self-Reliance. 'They must be of Caesar of Rome standing in the four parts of his empire. He's wearing a laurel crown in every one.'

'And look at the one which must depict Rome itself,' said Smith. 'He is holding a scroll in one hand. That must be telling us something.'

'Yes because *his world was fragmented* and his closest people turned on him in the end so *what was the value of his law,'* said Spontaneity.

'But he isn't holding anything in his other hand,' added Impulsiveness, who had left the corridor he was guarding to come and look at the picture.

'No, but he *is* pointing and that could be the *link in the chain* we must follow,' said Smith. 'What is he pointing at?'

The four of them followed the direction of Caesar's pointing arm and hand. On the opposite side of the wall set into a deep former window ledge was a large earthenware pot.

'A window which you can't see through,' said Smith.

Rushing over they discovered it to be full of water. But they could see something glinting inside. Smith reached into the water and pulled out a chain. Pulling it carefully out revealed four further chains each with a gold handle.

'Golden handles like on the gold cup in the picture!' said Spontaneous.

'Come on, we must pull them together,' said Smith.

As they all began to pull together there was a loud grating noise. The whole slab of floor, upon which the stone table stood, began to rise.

'Wait!' said Impulsiveness, 'We must stop. Giant Blame must have heard such a loud noise.'

'He who hesitates is lost!' shouted Smith. 'We cannot wait, now pull!'

With the four pulling the stone floor and table continued to slide easily across the room. As it did so the part of the floor directly in front of the fire also slid back revealing steps. Smith looked at Impulsiveness who was no longer pulling on his handle. *Recognise the weak link that impedes the strength of the whole,* were the words that came to him. Just in time he grasped at Impulsiveness' chain with his other hand as it was let go by Impulsiveness.

'The stones must be counterbalanced like the scales were in the picture!' shouted Smith. 'Quick we'll only have a few moments before our escape exit closes. Go!'

Spontaneity and Self-Reliance ran for the steps in front of the fire while Impulsiveness froze. 'But how do we know for certain that it is an exit! We might be imprisoned down there forever!' he protested.

At that moment, the booming voice of Giant Blame was heard to call out from down the corridor.

'Come on! Follow me!' shouted Smith and ran straight for the steps, Impulsiveness went with him. Almost as soon as they reached the bottom of the steps the stone entrance swung back to its former position. The light was not good but the air on their faces told them that the outside could not be far away.

With adrenaline keeping them going, not a word was said as they made their way through their dark passage. They all heard a faint noise that became increasingly louder. In a short while their path was blocked by a wall of water that sparkled before them from the morning sunlight that was clearly shining beyond it.

'So this is what it means to walk through a wall to freedom' said Smith to the others as he went to go through the waterfall first. 'And now to fortune!'

<<< AGENT SMITH FILE NOTE >>>

1. Remain unconcerned about trivia.

2. Chase your passion, not your pension.

3. Use creativity to do it, not to get out of it.

4. Recognise the weak link impeding the strength of the whole.

5. Do not be deceived by what you perceive.

6. Focus on opportunities, not obstacles.

7. When you take the easy path, you lose strength.

8. When you know your mind seizing the moment comes naturally.

9. Life is not accountable to us; we are accountable to Life.

007

ENTERING GOOD FORTUNE

'THIS IS NOT THE FIRST TIME THAT I HAVE had to retrace my steps,' said Smith to Self-Reliance, as the four of them made their way back to the turnstile. 'And on each occasion it could have been avoided simply by focusing more on where I am going.'

'Awareness is everything,' replied Self-Reliance. 'But don't be too hard on yourself because our detour provided the opportunity to develop both attention and intention.'

'And to develop our leadership attributes and teambuilding skills which I had not realised were so critical to success,' said Smith. 'Learning how to direct yourself through leadership builds character and the individual's strength of character is the best input he, or she, can bring to a team.'

'Agreement about what we wanted to achieve was important to me,' said Spontaneity. 'When the time came to act quickly we did so together.'

'I wish I had realised the importance,' put in Impulsiveness, 'but, when we needed to act as a team, I lost faith and thought that we were done for.'

'But your input in deciphering the inscriptions was important,' said Smith.

'Maybe, but you three would have worked them out without me, as you will reach Prosperity,' said Impulsiveness.

'Are you not coming with us then?' asked Smith.

'I'm not ready yet,' replied Impulsiveness. 'You three are confident about what you want and why you want it. But, I don't know what is important to me and indeed to be honest, I only came along because I was externally influenced and got excited about doing something different. But I realise its pointless doing something different if you don't know why you're doing it, so I'm going to take some time to discover what it is that will really motivate me.'

'Will you go back to Superficial?' asked Spontaneity, as the turnstile that led back to their former path came into view.

'I don't think taking a step back will do me any good. No, I think I'll visit some friends in the State of Chaos. They say that many people who have lived there for a short while leave there with a firm sense of direction. Perhaps that's just the environment that I need. Who knows, we may meet again one day, eh?'

'Look,' interrupted Spontaneity whose eye had caught sight of something on the side of the path as they had reached the turnstile. 'It's the signpost for the State of Limbo.'

'Well, no wonder we overlooked it, thrown in the hedge like that,' said Self-Reliance. 'And I'd say that it was hidden on purpose. Perhaps in the hope that it would distract people from their path.'

'Perhaps,' answered Smith. 'But in all honesty, it was our own fault.'

❑   ❑   ❑

HAVING SAID GOODBYE TO IMPULSIVENESS, the remaining team now continued along their original path. Despite the frequent obstacles before them, none of them complained. Firm in their shared sense of direction they took the opportunity to reflect on their recent experiences and to appreciate what they had learned.

'What doesn't break you certainly makes you! Obstacles don't obstruct, they instruct. So long as we become aware of how, why and where they have come about,' said Smith. 'How I could ever have aspired to become an agent with Secret Service without embarking on a process of personal development, I just don't know. The two go together like a hand and a glove. What is the use of a customer service ethos, without an awareness of a personal ethos?'

'Exactly, but then ask most companies what their customer service ethos is and they will look at you blankly. Unless they copy it from a competitor, most businesses just don't have one,' said Self-Reliance.

'And how can a marketing strategy be effective, if the creators of it are not in tune with themselves or their customers? Unless we are prepared to invest our genuine emotional energy in what we do, how will we ever develop the right behaviour and attitudes for the people we serve? We can't unless we become, and want to become, attentive to their needs. Learning to pay complete attention to customers has to be the key for developing customer loyalty,' added Smith.

'The biggest challenge for everyone involved in service has got to be to keep their mind on the person they are either serving, or are there to serve' said Spontaneity.

'It's amazing how many people in the service industry view customers as a nuisance. It's as though people either forget, or don't realise, who pays their salaries,' said Smith. 'Sometimes they are entirely unaware of the customer before them. No one likes to be ignored but when you ignore a customer you might as well just dehumanise them.'

'Yet on those rare occasions when you meet someone who genuinely pays you attention, you spend the whole day feeling good, because another person has emotionally energised you with their sincere and full attention,' said Self-Reliance.

'Listen! This will be basis of our customer ethos!' exclaimed Smith and as he spoke he wrote down the words:

'Taking a genuine interest in our customer; sincerely delivering the very best attention; emotionally energising them with good feelings because we make it clear that we value them, and enjoying the opportunity to offer great service to them.'

'Just think what an incredible business we would have, irrespective of what we provided, with such an ethos that injected such positive energy into every single transaction.' Smith continued, 'Remember people don't want to be sold to, but they like buying. And they buy people not things. That's what develops customer loyalty. Genuinely making them feel good for buying from you and by serving them with the solutions that they want.'

'This is a business that could only grow in strength, both in customers and reputation,' replied Self-reliance. 'It would be welcomed in Service City if we were to live there.'

'Then, when we get there, let's do just that!' proposed Spontaneity.

Absorbed in the firming up of a vision of what they wanted to do, encapsulating their purpose into a meaningful mission with values and guiding principles, and developing their strategy in line with a customer focused ethos, they did not notice that the road had become progressively easier. The rough ground beneath their feet had become smooth and the surrounding country was much more verdant and rich. The more they planned, the more unified, communicative and enthusiastically confident they became as individuals and as a team. Unconcerned about what obstacles may lie ahead of them they paid attention to what was important to them, focusing only on what they could do, not once thinking about how something couldn't be done.

▫   ▫   ▫

WITH THEIR RIGHT MOTIVES, FIRM RESOLVE, determined persistence, and enthusiastic confidence they had entered Good Fortune. Sensing they had done so, they looked about them calmly and immediately saw Opportunity.

'Welcome!' said Opportunity, 'I've been expecting you and knew that you would soon come across me. I am here to take you to The Agency at Business Incentive Park just a short way ahead, where everyone is expecting you.'

'Who exactly?' asked Smith. 'And how can they be expecting us?'

'Independence, Intrepid and Innovate of course,' answered Opportunity. 'They are the cousins of Intuition and Integrity. Intuition knew you would reach here and asked his cousins to expect you. They are looking forward to sharing much with you over the next couple of days. Afterwards, they will place you on your way to Prosperity and Service City.'

'So Good Fortune is here at last!' said Smith enthusiastically.

'It is,' replied Opportunity. 'And I am very pleased to have the chance to meet you here myself.'

'I am pleased to see you, too, because apparently we just missed each other at Accountability Base. You crossed the path of Redundant, shortly before my arrival, and introduced him to Enthusiasm. Bad timing on my part, I suppose,' added Smith laughingly.

'But not for Redundant his timing was just perfect, as was Enthusiasm's whom I usually meet with at most of the places I visit, and with many of the people I help. He's a good friend of mine. I just wish he could be with me more often, particularly when I bump into those people who seem to just want to ignore me.'

Opportunity then turned towards Spontaneity and smiled. 'But I have met with you before, haven't I?'

'You have indeed,' replied the other. 'It was when I was leaving my home town of Frankness and you were kind enough to direct me to Freedom Road.'

'That must surely be a good few years ago now, mustn't it?' asked Opportunity. 'How come it has taken so long for you to get here?'

'I'm afraid that it is more years than I care to remember, but my perception of Superficial Life as a young man led me to believe that I had arrived at Prosperity.'

'And what we perceive we allow to deceive. When our delusion becomes our reality it can be nearly impossible to see ourselves as we are. So what prompted you to start out again?' enquired Opportunity.

'I happened to look into the mirror longer than usual one morning,' said Spontaneity. 'The face looking back at me was like a stranger.'

'Well, you must have succeeded in discovering your old self, or rather young self again. Indeed, it must have been your true self you rediscovered, because I easily recognised you,' said Opportunity. 'As I often say to those I meet, it can never be too late to follow your heart and seek Good Fortune.'

Opportunity turned to Self-Reliance and said, 'Now, I *know* that you and I have met many times before. Sometimes you have chosen to walk with me along a path, and others you have decided to travel alone.'

'There have been occasions when I have been so occupied with someone else that your company was the last thing I felt I needed,' answered Self-Reliance.

'I know you refer to meeting with my twin brother Adversity,' commented Opportunity. 'Though we tend to travel the same path, he prefers to stay slightly ahead of me and consequently often meets with people before I do.'

'But I had no idea that you were related to that rogue, Adversity?'

'Not many people do, though I have to say he is no rogue. When you get to know him better he's actually a great teacher. Believe it or not he told me that you had left Prosperity, but he was certain you would return.'

'Yes, but no thanks to him!' Self-Reliance said. 'It was his influence that made me leave Prosperity the last time!'

'Maybe, but you have returned stronger than when you previously left. You seem to have lost the arrogance and pride that Adversity told me you carried around with you. They were partly the reasons he visited you the last time.'

'You're right,' sighed Self-Reliance. 'Indeed leaving Prosperity was very much my own fault. I felt that I did not need the help of others, as I thought I could do everything on my own. Now I have learned the importance of channelling my strengths to release my potential, rather than impede it.'

'Unfortunately too many people in the world neither achieve what was expected of them, nor enjoy what they themselves hope for,' said Opportunity. 'Although the infinite possibilities that exist in the world are great, the probabilities of them ever being utilised are small. What our world needs are like-minded individuals that channel their strengths for a meaningful purpose. Individuals who choose to build their success on the success of others through bringing opportunities to others and by making the most of their own opportunities.'

❏   ❏   ❏

BUSINESS INCENTIVE PARK WAS COMPOSED of elegant buildings aesthetically placed around excellent facilities. The ambience was one of pleasant harmony and orderly discipline yet considerate and resourceful.

Independence, Intrepid and Innovate delivered a genuinely warm welcome.

'It's great to arrive at a place where you're fully appreciated,' said Opportunity.

'I must say that it's a new experience for me,' said Smith. 'I don't believe I have ever been made so welcome before.'

'Whether you have customers or guests, there is only one-way to welcome them. And that is the right way!' said Innovate. 'What we enjoy doing here is thinking up ways of how we can continuously improve on that *right* way.'

'Many of the creative suggestions made here are recognised in Service City, so it is worth you taking special attention of them,' said Opportunity. 'As for me I must take my leave of you, for the moment, as I am due to meet with some other good friends in Prosperity.'

'We will see you again though, won't we?' asked Spontaneity.

'Now that you have entered Good Fortune you can see me whenever you want to. And I can promise you that you'll see even more of me in Prosperity and Service City itself as I have a home there. So, I'll look forward to seeing you soon.'

'We'll all look forward to that too,' said Smith. Then, turning back to Innovate he said, 'I would like to hear more about your ideas.'

'First and foremost,' replied Innovate, 'great service requires continuous questioning of existing routines and trying to create something that brings meaningful value. Routine service is something that customers soon take for granted and therefore don't value. Consequently whatever you do in a routine way will not impress your customers.

'Business has a tendency to treat customer relations as just a routine operation. These routines lack emotion and when a service is devoid of emotion customers notice and place no value on it.'

❑   ❑   ❑

'WHAT IS THE DIFFERENCE between routine service and Secret Service?' Smith asked.

'Over the next few days you will learn most of the secrets of service,' said Innovate. 'And as you understand that personal growth is linked with giving better-than-excellent service, you will be able to appreciate and apply what you learn. For now, though, let me give you an example of what is thought to be service, yet is simply a routine.

'Imagine you take your car in for its service. When you return to collect it you find everything as you expected. The car is ready, the price is about what you expected and the way you are greeted, dealt with and leave is as you expected. A routine inspection begets a routine expectation, but such routine is not actually service. For whatever is expected cannot be service. Only when there is unexpected benefit and added value can it begin to be deemed service.

'Now, let us imagine that in arranging to take your car in for service, you are unexpectedly offered to have it collected for you, given a loan car and have your own car brought back to you when it is ready. When it is returned your car is in sparkling condition from a full valet and on the seat a small gift has been left with the compliments of the management. Also on the seat is a copy of the work sheet, showing the tasks performed, together with a short hand written note from the actual mechanic responsible for carrying out the service, saying all is in order and thanking you for your custom. Having been advised by the garage in advance what the service charge will be, you are further pleased to see that what you pay is not more. At all times during collection and delivery you are treated with genuine polite friendliness. *That's* service. And what do you do? You become an ambassador for that garage and tell all your friends. You feel good, you feel safe and you feel valued.'

'Wow! I can't believe that such service could ever exist and even if it did, that people would be nice about providing it,' said Spontaneity.

'The responsibility of business leaders is to educate every one of their people in the importance of putting emotional value into what they do. This they can do by treating their own employees in the same way as their best clients, because they in turn are the businesses front-line to the customers. And with the dawning of the new customer reign they will have to do this in order to keep their competitive advantage and build their co-operative reputation.

'Already at Service City you do not even have to make the call to request service. The computer chip within your car registers when servicing is required, whether it is tyres, exhaust, battery, engine, gearbox of whatever, and informs the garage of your choice directly. Your garage serves you automatically to maintain its own business reputation, as their chip also notifies the manufacturer of the vehicle as well as other competitors who may be seeking your business.

'Then it is only the behaviour and attitude of a business that retains the customer's loyalty. A customer must not experience being treated as another transaction or a statistic on a survey sheet. They will be looking for the emotional value that is genuinely put into building a relationship with them, and the creativity of service. Creativity is closely related to integrity, because developing ways that give more is synonymous with creating trust.

'Trust, of course, is the very foundation of any lasting relationship. When you are building trust it is vital that you deliver what you promise to others, whether they are friends or customers. Indeed, why would you want to treat a customer any different to how you would behave toward a friend anyway?

'To go further, why would you want to charge your customers for any additional service, when you wouldn't charge a friend? Say you were to buy a car from the garage that I have just spoken about in Service City, and late one night you break your key off in the lock. One call to this garage and their twenty-four hour service will come and fix it for you, without charging. Now they may charge for something slightly more serious, but their whole customer ethos is based on providing the same kind of service for customers as they would for a good friend.

'In Service City businesses strive to turn one-time buyers into lifetime customers. Keeping their customers for life by offering free, friendly service for certain peace of mind jobs makes better sense to them than paying huge advertising sums to build an image that they hope will win customers.

'The majority of businesses in the world who want to provide good service, however, fall into a difficult trap that is hard to get out of. Because they want to improve their service, as they believe it to be the key to more sales, they have a tendency to promise *too* much. In doing so they raise the expectations of their potential customers who understandably feel let down, even cheated, when delivery does not match up to the promise.'

'Marketing promises are seldom lived up to,' said Smith.

'When the product excels the description in the brochure you feel that you have really got something special,' said Spontaneity.

'No business can ever blame the customer for being disappointed, because it can only be the business' own fault,' continued Innovate. 'And it doesn't matter how sincere the business' intentions were, the fact is that if they don't keep their word, they are letting their customer down. To over promise and under deliver is sadly, just "business as *usual*". Such *normality* is of course not conducive to competitive advantage. The only way for business to provide good service is to operate *unusually* which means always delivering whatever is promised or, even better, delivering more. Ultimately customers do not want sincere apologies, they want you to deliver what you promised.

'The only source of competitive advantage that a business has is its employees and the service they provide. Therefore all front-line people must be trained to ask themselves a certain question when dealing with customers. And that is: "How would my action look on Tomorrow's Headline?"

'The most important thing that interests a customer is, did you deliver what you promised you would, because that is what prompted them to buy from you. Keeping your word is worth more than all the sincere apologies and make-it-up-to-you gifts in the world. These individual employee ethics of course require that every single employee must have the authority of the chairman when dealing with the customer in order to resolve their problem. Because good customer service that builds loyalty is just far too important to be passed to some customer relations department. Everybody must be a customer service ambassador for their company.

❑   ❑   ❑

'PEOPLE WHO WORK IN SERVICE CITY are all ambassadors for their particular business through choice first,' continued Innovate. 'And like any good ambassador they are absolutely sure about what they do and why they do it. They do not consider that they sell products; they consider themselves as catalysts for turning every one of their one-time customers that choose to buy from them, into lifetime customers.

'How do they go about this? By doing everything they can to make the customer feel good about doing business with them. They only consider what *can* be done for the customer, never what *can't* be done.'

'But what if what the customer asks is unreasonable, from a cost point of view?' asked Self-Reliance.

'Ninety-nine percent of the time the customer requests only small details. Yet, it is the little things that count in service, never the big things. Imagine, for example, purchasing something and then finding when you got home that it was faulty. You would not be very happy, particularly if you had made a special trip to buy it. Upon contacting the business, however, imagine how you would feel if the person who sold you the item called you straight back, apologised for your inconvenience and promised to arrange for another to be delivered to your home that very day. And then phoned you in the evening to make sure you received it.

'Now that may cost the business more than the product value, but it would be a considerably smaller amount than the amount required in advertising costs to build a good image to improve customer relations. Because an immediate solution to the problem had been provided, your loyalty to that business would begin to grow. The value of a loyal customer who is more than happy to be an ambassador for a business is immeasurable.'

'In that situation the customer was clearly in the right, but is the customer always right?' asked Smith. 'I know that one of my colleagues, Cynical, would argue that the product might have been in good order but that it more than likely stopped working because of improper use by the customer.'

'Those businesses engaged in offering service to others cannot be expected to hide behind the clause *caveat emptor*, let the buyer beware, if they want to develop a competitive advantage,' replied Innovate. 'Secret Service expects scrupulous honesty, so why should the buyer of a product or service, that marketing, or an assistant has stimulated them to purchase, have to be wary? A customer's role is simple. It is to enjoy the benefits of a purchase and not to suffer because of its defects.

'As for being right, well, the customer may not always be right, but what they have to say must be valued. So it follows that the customer is always right up to a point. The secret is to decide what that point should be, because the more a business is prepared to give the customer the benefit of the doubt, the more profitable it will be in the long-term. But let me give you another example.

❑   ❑   ❑

'I RECALL BEING IN A STORE where several items were on special offer when I overheard an irate customer demand she be reimbursed for an item she bought the previous week, an item that was now selling on offer. Her argument was that if she had waited a week she would have saved the difference anyway. The assistant she spoke to gave the small amount of money involved without hesitation. Contented, the woman started to collect some other items that were on offer.

'The point is that if you want to keep a customer's business, and encourage them to buy more, then you should give them exactly what they ask for without hesitation. If you do anything less you might as well offer them nothing, because you'll have lost their good will. Remember, the ethos of the Secret Service Agency you aspire to join is that giving better-than-excellent service is not a matter of doing customers a favour; it's a way of life.

'Creative service always beats procedural service in the contest to give the best. Use your initiative, not the rulebook, to solve your customer's problems. Even when customers may be wrong, or taking advantage, do not show them that you think they are. Simply use creative service to resolve their problem, because though rigid procedural service may allow you to win one-time, you will most certainly lose a lifetime customer. The maxim you should follow is: Thoughtful service costs less than thoughtless service.

'There are course times when an obnoxious customer is so outrageously unfair and difficult that you will choose to refuse to serve him or her. But though these occasions are rare, too often they seem to form the basis of how to deal with people. Service procedures focus on how to handle difficult customers *instead* of how to be friendly with people. Consequently, staff are always preparing themselves for the difficult situations, rather than focusing on how to make the majority of their customer service more effective.

'We must always try to look for the good in others, even if we are let down, rather than be wary of people because we assume they may be difficult. 1% of difficult customers should not form the basis of how 99% percent are treated.

'Good customer service is the most effective form of advertising. People will buy from you and keep coming back to you in preference to your competition because of good service. They will constantly reward you through the praises they extol about your business. This word of mouth marketing is worth a fortune.'

'Consistent delivery of good service must be difficult to achieve though,' said Smith.

'Consistent good service builds goodwill. And it is of course the goodwill of a business that can make it *so* valuable,' replied Innovate. 'For example, it does not make you feel good when you have recommended a restaurant to your friends only to learn that they did not enjoy it. Even worse is when you accompany your friends and you are treated like a stranger at the establishment you have praised, the service is poor and the food is average. Since every business is as strong as its weakest link, the best way to ensure that you consistently deliver is to encourage your people to go the extra mile. Such action turns reasonable service into better-than-excellent service.'

❑   ❑   ❑

'YOU HAVE ALREADY LEARNED that you cannot serve others effectively until you have learned how to serve yourself by being the best you can be through consistent personal development. This follows the principle that leadership and management function more effectively through example, rather than by just procedures and systems. It is pointless to engage in recruiting and training the best available people, if you do not live and breath that which you want your people to do.

'Business cannot deliver better-than-excellent service if the management do not *really* believe in it. They must train people to use their own judgement rather than stick rigidly to rules. Development of their judgement will come from knowing why they are doing what they are doing, and aligning it with how they communicate with their customers.'

'If they don't know what they want, then their judgement will reflect it of course,' said Self-Reliance. 'When a person is unsure they become so judgmental they are unable to use their judgement.'

'Which is why training is so important even if the person being trained may only stay a short period,' said Innovative. 'You will discover at Secret Service that every front-line person that has first contact with the customer, whether they are receptionists, car park attendants, waiters, shop assistants, receptionists and call centre respondents, undergoes regular training on friendly customer service. They appraise themselves and are appraised by both colleagues and customers every week. Managers and leaders do the same because they see it as setting the right example for their people.'

'The only appraisals I have heard of are done on an annual basis with the focus on what was wrong,' said Smith. 'As for getting their customers to appraise, well that's unheard of. How do you go about doing that?'

'Every business in Service City understands that the best way to keep customers is to regularly ask what they like or dislike about the service offered,' replied Innovate. 'They don't send or give out time-consuming surveys, because no one likes filling in forms. That's why guarantees are seldom filled in because they are not simple to do. Only companies that are not interested in developing lifetime customers insist on seeing a guarantee before helping you.

'Being asked just a couple of different questions politely on a regular basis, however, is something that any customer is more than happy to do. But it isn't just front-line people. Everyone asks their particular customers such questions, whether they are internal or external to the business.

Questions like:

How well do we deliver what we promise?
How accessible are we when you contact us?
How well do we listen to you?
Are we helpful and polite?
Are we doing anything that annoys you?
Do you think we take you for granted?
Do you ever recommend us?

□ □ □

'GREAT PEOPLE GIVE GREAT CUSTOMER SERVICE, which in turn brings great rewards!' said Independence who now joined them. 'So the best employees are always those who have an attitude of responsibility and enjoy a good degree of autonomy in what they do. Employees must be made aware of the importance of their role at the outset. Their training must raise their expectations of what can be achieved. They must appraise themselves regularly and, most importantly, they must be praised for what they do and be well rewarded. Companies that give better-than-excellent service *reward* their people for delivering it. So, it's a case of, raise, appraise and praise your people right and they'll treat your customers right.'

'That's music to my ears,' said Self-Reliance. 'But it strikes me that though many businesses may be very quick to tell their people how special they are to them, their actual recognition and reward always seem to be lacking. Even worse, some businesses seem intent on reprimanding their staff when service is *poor*, but say nothing when service is *good*.'

'Often a business that wants long-term growth will hope for better service and greater loyalty, but have a reward system that is linked to speed and sales total,' answered Innovate. 'Strategy is focused on the long-term profits, which is what the former will deliver, whereas bonuses are paid only on the short-term, which is what the latter is based. Employees, therefore, will focus on short-term budgets instead of long-term growth.

'The point is that whatever is rewarded gets done. Business will not get from its people what it may hope for. It will only get from them what it rewards.'

'So reward the right behaviour and enjoy the results. Fail to reward and praise the right behaviour and you don't enjoy the results,' said Self-Reliance.

'Exactly,' agreed Independence. 'If you are in business and you are uncertain about how an individual is performing, then look at the sort of rewards they can expect. Because, however it is set up, it will influence their behaviour. A business may hire employees and managers to serve customers face to face, but then 'reward' them with a low flat hourly wage and provide little, or no, training in the basics of how to provide good service. The reward, therefore, may as well be interpreted as simply 'minding the shop.' As for those people that are employed in support of the customer but have no actual contact with them, any customer linked reward or recognition for effort is non-existent.'

'It seems ridiculous that many businesses offer little training and pay to the front-line positions, yet expect them to give excellent service,' said Spontaneity.

'So, what exactly needs to be rewarded to ensure that all your employees are customer focused and what must you do to achieve it?' asked Smith.

'First and foremost a customer focused business must have a reward system that expressly rewards its employees or ambassadors, as we call our people, for rewarding customers by providing excellent service. Secondly, leaders must set the example through their own customer-oriented performance. But before I explain the type of reward system required for your people, always remember that winning and keeping customers depends on rewarding your customers for being customers.

❑   ❑   ❑

'IMAGINE FOR EXAMPLE THAT YOU OPEN a new restaurant. Everyone is excited yet nervous, and wants to make everything work out well. When the doors first open everyone rewards customers for booking and arriving with highly attentive service, thoughtful behaviour and a friendly welcoming attitude. Within a few months your business is performing really well, with customers returning again and again and new ones pouring in. You start to feel confident because there is so much business to handle and though you may have been a bit abrupt with that last customer, you don't concern yourself too much because there are plenty more coming through the door. But it's at this point that the paradox of success begins to materialise.

'In the ensuing months you are the last to realise that the attention to customers, the quality of service and the intention to perform as well as possible has insidiously declined. With fewer customers and falling sales you keep behind the scenes, busy devising cost cutting plans, special offers and writing copy for some advertising that someone has suggested you really ought to do. You lay off a couple of former ambassadors, reduce the portions of the meals, rationalising that they were far too generous before, but still the customers don't come back. You blame the economy, the weather and the new competition that has just opened so that you feel that it's not your fault. But the fact remains that it is.

'You stopped rewarding the customers and they voted with their feet. In the beginning you made them feel so special, and they liked it and supported your business by coming back again and telling their friends. Then, when business boomed, you began to take them for granted and they withdrew their support. It's that simple. Now, perhaps if you had rewarded your ambassadors nothing would have changed and the business would have continued to grow. When your focus changed you stopped driving the business, but continued running it into the ground. Your ambassadors simply followed your example.'

'A reward system is certainly the crucial ingredient for a successful business,' said Smith.

'A simple ingredient, yet, almost always overlooked,' replied Independence. 'Progress is Man's ability to complicate simplicity and in the chase for it, Man forgets what drives his fellow man to do things. So many people run their homes and business on the basis of communicating to their children, spouses, friends, colleagues and ambassadors, when they have done something wrong, or forgotten to attend to something. Management wrapped in hidden agendas and office politics, tends to find fault and any form of praise is looked upon as a weakness. Yet, we all know that a short statement of praise makes us double our efforts with a renewed vigour – simply so that we can receive more of the same.

'With our inherent craving for meaning and purpose, whenever we receive praise for our efforts or rewards for achieving our goals, we feel valued. Therefore, good business management always starts with clearly communicated expectations, as to the kind of behaviour and results they want. Furthermore, it ensures that absolutely every ambassador has concrete, specific goals. Getting everyone, not just customer contact ambassadors but *everyone*, to ask themselves *'What results do I produce and do they benefit the customer?'* encourages everyone to think about the basics of their job in terms of the customer.

'Everyone should be encouraged and guided into setting their own goals. These goals must be simple and to the point. Each person should only have a couple of goals to focus on at any one time and they should be concisely written for clarity of purpose and commitment. Above all, they must be measurable.'

'Since, if they are not measurable, they cannot be a goal,' put in Innovate. 'Some people will always argue that what they do is just not measurable. Well, when it comes to customer driven service everything can be measurable. And we can only recognise improvement if something is measurable.'

'And if you can't recognise improvement how can you reward the effort involved?' continued Independence. 'A system manager, for example, may establish that his role is to co-ordinate effective procedures to ensure that all the right products ordered reach the customer right on time and in the right place. His measurable goal would be to reduce the amount of times ambassadors complain about the system by twenty-five percent, with follow up goals over a set period to continue to do the same thing. Everyone will benefit starting with the customer, but including the system manager's fellow ambassadors and the business which can only continue to grow.'

'Goals and measures will only start ambassadors moving in the right direction of course,' said Innovate. 'You then need specific rewards that will keep them moving. Rewards that they know they will receive at the appropriate time and not some time later.'

'Absolutely! The right rewards for the right behaviour guarantees continuation of the right results,' said Independence. 'Unfortunately, even though some businesses may have goal-setting programmes, when they are not linked in with a specific reward system the programmes fail. And you can imagine what undesired results soon follow with the additional difficulty of low morale.

'Each goal must be linked into a reward when it is achieved. In many organisations it is only sales managers and teams that receive commission bonuses. But in linking specific rewards to all goals that have been established, teams and individuals can share in the same benefits. The system manager, for example, will be rewarded for reducing complaints by each twenty five percent he achieves. But these rewards are of course conditional. For maintained enthusiastic effort on a regular basis there must be something more.'

□   □   □

'AND THERE IS,' SAID INNOVATE. 'Many stores in Service City employ mystery shoppers whose sole purpose is to catch ambassadors doing just the right thing. They are not interested in what he, or she, may be doing incorrectly as that is not their role. They are there as customers and when they see ambassadors performing well they immediately praise the ambassador and give him, or her, a cash reward. And the incident is posted to management for special recognition.'

'Wow!' exclaimed Spontaneity. 'The ambassador must feel incredible, praised in front of customers and peers like that. But that's almost unheard of. You would have thought that the mystery shopper would be there to catch the ambassador out and put him, or her, right about where they were going wrong.'

'It is much better to reward ambassadors for doing what you want them to do, instead of continually reprimanding them for doing what you don't want. And of course when you do reward them, everyone else makes even more of an effort to achieve their goals and receive 'unexpected' rewards.

'As you said when a manager gives on the spot praise in public, the ambassador feels good. But should the manager castigate the ambassador in public, the ambassador will only feel resentment and he will feel that his day is just full of gloom and doom. Castigation can be done at the right time and in the right place and put in such a way that it does not hurt an individual, and explain why his, or her, behaviour was not in the interests of the team. In other words positive feedback on improving behaviour is provided. That is another reason why appraisals must be done on a regular basis and not on an annual basis.'

'You say every one is always an ambassador, even if they never interact with customers. What about those always behind the scenes?' asked Smith.

'Not *every* salesperson may be an ambassador, but every ambassador is a customer-focused salesperson because, regardless of their role they are an envoy, representing the business they work with,' began Independence. 'Those who are employed behind the scenes, however, cannot always understand how they can be salespeople until it is pointed out to them. Let me give you an example.

'When a new hotel was about to open at Service City we were invited to give a talk on creative customer service. Of the four hundred new people involved that made up housekeeping, engineering, security, reception and operating employees, banqueting and restaurant, we were told that there were just five salespeople. In establishing the desired results, the measured goals and the reward and recognition programme, we suggested that every one of the four hundred employees, and not just those involved in sales, should be an ambassador for their hotel by talking about the benefits it offered to whoever asked. Giving a person a sense of pride in what they do by giving them a piece of the action with a reward is a tremendous motivator and energy builder.

'So, we then suggested that everyone try to get *one* room booked per year without pressure, but through word of mouth, and each person would be rewarded with a commission. Well, the response was phenomenal, everyone knew someone and all they needed to do was to get one room booked. Because what was asked of them seemed reasonable, as well as attainable, everyone bought into it. Everyone became an ambassador, with some departments even working together in teams and agreeing to pool their future rewards. Some achieved much more, but every one of the four hundred achieved at least a single occupancy as suggested. They all enjoyed success and the benefits of both reward and recognition. As for the service it became outstanding because, as there was always a guest staying that one colleague had recommended, everyone strove to be the best they could possibly be. Everyone is now a committed ambassador because they get rewarded for doing what they get paid for anyway, which is looking after the customer.'

'That's where we must stay when we arrive at the Capital,' said Smith. 'I can't wait to experience such service! Mind you, that's if they have any rooms left!'

'Oh don't worry they will be able to accommodate you as they always keep rooms for both regular and new customers. If they can't they will arrange for you to stay at another hotel as well as a complimentary car to take you there.'

'Wow, when you make your people ambassadors and reward them accordingly, they must feel like winners,' said Spontaneity.

'Everyone loves to be part of a winning team!' said Intrepid who came in carrying refreshments. 'Give people a piece of the action and they'll think 'customer.'

Give them work they love to do and reward them well for doing it and they'll think 'customer.' Build in promotion and increased responsibilities, but with the freedom to steer their own goals toward fulfilment, and they'll think 'customer.' Give them incentives in the form of prizes, whether tickets to the theatre and sport events, dinners or even holidays and they'll think 'customer.' Make them feel that they're part of something special, part of something fun, yet something that is making a difference in the quality of the lives of others.'

'Even holidays?' said Self-Reliance.

'Absolutely, because it takes financial courage to treat your people like that and they accept without question that the customer must always come first,' replied Intrepid. 'Some businesses in Service City have actually purchased holiday homes for their ambassadors to enjoy using. They consider this investment as *vital*.

'Good business acknowledges that rewarding the customer is *everyone's* responsibility and rewarding those who look after the customer is the responsibility of management. But it takes courage to operate your business by always putting customers first, something Secret Service is well aware of.'

❑   ❑   ❑

DURING THE NEXT TWO DAYS SMITH and his colleagues consolidated their understanding of how to give better-than-excellent service. Full of enthusiasm for what lay ahead of them, they were then taken to the highest point of Good Fortune. From there they were able to see quite clearly the final road to Prosperity and actually see the tallest towers of the capital, Service City.

'There before you lies your goal and your future,' said Independence. 'The Founder, Customer, is demanding but fair and advocates that self-government is the best form of government. There you will experience a level of Secret Service that has long been forgotten in the State of Mediocrity.

'To finally see Prosperity and glimpse Service City makes me value all the challenges I have endured on the road to get here,' said Smith. 'What lies before you will make your journey worthwhile, but remember that you have been able to reach it because of what lies within you,' said Intrepid. 'Having the courage of your own convictions, despite what you may come up against, will always provide you with your just reward.'

'I have not seen Prosperity from such a high point before,' said Self-Reliance. 'Tell me, what is that deep cut in the land between here and there?'

'That is the Chasm of Professional Complacency which you will have to cross with care,' replied Intrepid. 'There is a bridge, though you cannot see it from here. Follow the path and you will come directly to it. However, keep your mind on what you are looking for, as some people forget and are *still* trying to get across it. You should also be aware that, surrounding the Capital, there is a river to cross. It is known as River of Insults. Be careful that before you reach your goal, you do not get swept away by it, as many aspiring agents have before.'

'Isn't there a bridge over this river?' asked Spontaneity.

'No,' Intrepid answered. 'You must pass through it, so hold your head high and keep your head above the water.'

'Well, our goal in sight,' said Smith. 'Let's go!'

<<< AGENT SMITH FILE NOTE >>>

1. Treating customers as transactions devalues your service.

2. Question routines and rules taken for granted.

3. Focus on turning one-time buyers into lifetime customers.

4. It is the little things that make a difference.

5. Never show your customer that they may be wrong.

6. Reward the right behaviour to get the right result.

7. Be an ambassador as that is how your customer sees you.

8. Thoughtful service costs less than thoughtless service.

9. Ask your customers what *they* think of your service.

008

ARRIVING AT SERVICE CITY

'THAT HAS TO HAVE BEEN THE BEST TIME SINCE I left the City of Apathy!' exclaimed Smith, walking briskly between his two travelling companions. 'We have learned so many valuable service keys. To think that so many businesses operate without them.'

'Giving better-than-excellent service is certainly more rewarding for everyone,' said Self-Reliance. 'Yet the majority of businesses treat the customer and employees in a way that directly opposes what giving great service requires.'

'It does seem that getting employees to serve a system is standard, instead of adapting the system to serve the employees who in turn serve the customers,' said Spontaneity. 'Yet though customers will know a business for what it really is, the business is too often unaware of how they are perceived. Customer service is ultimately about choice. What makes a business successful is the choices customers make about it, and the way a business encourages both its ambassadors and customers through training and reward.'

'That's right, except that you may not be able to train your customers as you can your ambassadors,' said Smith.

'I don't see why not,' replied Spontaneity. 'After all, the best way to turn a one-time buyer into a lifetime customer is to reward them for being a customer. And where there is reward there must also be training because it follows on. We have learned that the best reward is to be a genuine friend acting thoughtfully with attentive understanding to our customer, so they feel good about the way we serve them. By consistently giving such service we are in effect training them to return to us again and again out of their own choice.'

'Yes, that is true,' admitted Smith. 'As customers, we do feel more confidant when we have got to know the person we are dealing with and they make us feel valued and special. I can't wait to experience such friendly service ambassadors that have a passion to bring the very best to their customer.'

'Ridiculous!' exclaimed Analysis who had just appeared. 'Absolutely ludicrous! The very idea of allowing a customers' likes and dislikes to enter into the process of making business decisions is ludicrous, and goes against the rational backbone and logic framework that makes business what it is! I suggest you empty your head of stupid notions if you ever hope to cross this rift before you.'

'We believe that the *key* to success is to be a product of company policy,' added Paralysis, 'not to express your own feelings and thoughts, or listen to those of your customer. Customers are much more amenable and secure when they are told what to do.'

□   □   □

APPEARING SUDDENLY FROM A SHARP TURN in the path as they had, the team of Analysis Paralysis took Smith and his companions by surprise. Just slightly beyond the path plunged a huge chasm. It was not possible to clearly see the other side but Smith could make out a small footbridge in the distance.

'And when my colleague says 'key', he's right because we know all there is to know about customer service, business acumen and scientific management,' said Analysis. 'There isn't anything that we haven't either investigated or written a procedural report on. And there's nothing we have not measured in the form of efficient performance appraisals and total quality management either. So don't talk to us about the necessity for emotional input, empathy or reliable care because we're not interested. We've heard it all before and there's no reason or logic to it.'

'And if there's no logic to it then it won't work!' added Paralysis.

'Then why are you skulking around jumping out at people instead of living it up in Prosperity across from here?' demanded Smith confidently.

'Skulking around! Jumping out!' said Analysis. 'We have no reason to skulk or jump out! It's people like *you* that disturb the peace with your ideas of letting systems serve people instead of employees serving the system. We can transverse this rift before us whenever we want to! It's just that on examining the bridge it is clear that its thickness will not support its length. As good citizens we have submitted our report and are waiting here for something to be done. It would be illogical to do otherwise'

'Except we have not actually submitted our report yet,' corrected Paralysis. 'Because there are still a few points that we have to compile for its conclusion.'

'Which makes perfect sense but as soon as it is done, and we have both signed it off, it will be submitted,' returned Analysis.

'I've heard of you,' said Smith. 'You were a pupil of Discipline once, and a very precise one that enjoyed the deliberation of an obstacle in preference to actually surmounting it. And you,' added Smith looking at Paralysis, 'were a pupil of Persistence, but your insistence on perfection has always stopped you from reaching where you are going.'

'We are not the slightest bit concerned about what you have heard about us,' replied Analysis. 'Last year we both appraised each other in detail and are pleased with how we are doing, thank you.'

'Absolutely,' added Paralysis. 'But the real point is we know why *we* are here. We consider it our duty to ensure that agents have really examined why they are on this road in the first place. This is not a road for inspired, time wasting aspirants, you know.'

'By whose authority are you trying to stop us?' enquired Smith. 'We are here because we have earned our passage through by knowing what we stand for, and developing a strategy and customer ethos. If you are trying to make us pay a toll then our willingness to learn and understand secret service is all that we need to cross this bridge. A bridge that I and my friends are prepared to trust in regarding its strength and direction.'

'Strong confident words for someone who has not yet displayed what you profess to be secret service,' said Analysis. 'Our authority comes from the compilation of our own procedural report wherein we state that people who profess to walk their talk should be tested to the point of proof. Let us therefore imagine that I am your customer wishing to cross this bridge that you are so confident of. Are you prepared to submit to my questions? And, if you are, are you then prepared to accept the consequence of not crossing over should my assessment of your service be not acceptable? Indeed, shall we say accept even the consequence of others crossing in your place?'

For a moment Smith thoughts flew back to Discipline's words about how the Analysis Paralysis duo perceived their duty as one of confronting and questioning agents to see if they should really continue forward or turn back. He also remembered the danger of dealing with people with ulterior motives. But the fact was that he knew his motives and was therefore clearly able to see the motives of these two before him.

Unable to find away across themselves because they were so immersed in procedural and policy minutiae, they were out to take the place of Smith and his companions through stealing *their* confidence. These two were still looking for a way, even though they seem keener to stop others. Above all, though, he must have the courage of his convictions. There was no way that he was going to allow himself, or his friends for that matter, to be tricked, distracted, convinced, cajoled or persuaded from the their chosen path.

'I am prepared to submit to any questions that you might pose on the basis that when I answer correctly, you will straightaway stop confronting future agents on this road,' said Smith.

'But that is what I do,' said Analysis innocently. 'For how else can I myself walk my talk? After all, is it not right that we should have the courage to stick to our convictions?'

'With your capacity for examination wouldn't it be better to find out why customers are loyal to a business instead of why it is important for an employee to become a product of company policy?'

'But we have already agreed that you will submit to *my* questions, not I to yours. So your question is academic,' replied Analysis. 'Now then,' he added, 'answer me this. What is the established system for delivering business success?'

Smith began to list what he had learned to them, slowly and clearly. 'Remember, systems in themselves do not deliver success - it is the system makers that *must* have the desire to achieve it. So:

'One. Listen to Intuition.
'Two. Follow your heart.
'Three. Evaluate your motives.
'Four. Accept personal accountability.
'Five. Release frustration
'Six. Develop a charter.
'Seven. Overcome insecurity.
'Eight. Endure the Valleys of Discontent.
'Nine. Survive Superficial life.
'Ten. Don't hesitate to develop leadership and team direction.
'Eleven. Embrace opportunity.
'Twelve. Learn through self-government, courage and creativity.
'Then you understand how to give better-than-excellent service.'

□   □   □

SELF-RELIANCE AND SPONTANEITY cheered Smith, even though they were being glared at by Paralysis.

'Would you agree that in compliance with scientific evidence of management practices it is better for business to predict what products will sell, than know what customers will buy?' asked Analysis.

'I believe that all the scientific management pales into insignificance in comparison to understanding the needs, wants, likes and dislikes of a customer. Such a thing can only be achieved through attentive, friendly, reliable service, not through artificial procedures.'

'So, you believe that subjective emotions drive success with customers, rather than rational objectivity?' asked Analysis.

'Though goals and rewards must be measured, scientific management seeks to measure what people do, rather than what they achieve. Activity is therefore deemed more important than productivity. The person who sees ten customers in a day is considered more worthy than the person who takes time with just five. Yet, the latter is more inclined to develop the relations that the long-term strategy of a business hopes for. We are not machines that should follow some programme that rationalises that a certain amount of transactions must be dealt with in a certain way and in a certain period. Our ability to be influenced by our emotions and feelings make us the people that we are and achieve the things we do.

'The philosophy of pursuing rational objectivity in order to reach business decisions frowns upon the use of emotion, yet after all our massaging of figures and rationalisation of surveys we return to discover that our original *feeling* for something was right. Thus it is emotion that drives a business, a passionate emotion emanating from the belief and commitment of those driving it. People neither do what they do, nor buy what they buy because of logic. They do and buy because of how they feel, or how it makes them feel, and then apply rational thinking to justify what they do, or what they buy.

'If people do not believe in you, it's because you don't believe in yourself. True belief comes from how you feel about what you do, why you do it and how important it is to you. Such belief cannot be based on rational objectivity.'

'Hmmm, although I applaud your rhetoric, I cannot agree with either of your answers,' said Analysis. 'It demands too much of a change in my thinking. However, do not forget that I am your customer in this debate. Therefore, following your commitment to Secret Service, I must be right. So I win!'

'You win nothing,' returned Smith. 'For you have not asked any service of me, other than question my beliefs and integrity. Neither of those I compromised, nor did I offer you a disservice by misguiding you. Your test was to see if I would walk my talk. Well, for words to match deeds, allow my very commitment to cross this bridge, that you are so convinced is unsafe, to be the proof you require.'

'And we're with him,' added Self-Reliance and Spontaneity.

'Then you're crazy and deserve to fall into Professional Complacency like so many have before you that became overconfident in themselves,' scoffed Analysis. 'When you fall from that bridge you will meet many businesses that appear to be profitable in spite of themselves. But really they are going nowhere, believing they no longer have to try. Come take a look.'

As his companions went to the edge and Analysis pointed down into the depths of abyss, Smith shouted, 'Don't look down!' We must keep our minds on what we are looking for and not on what others have chosen to do.' With that Smith stepped on the bridge and began to walk confidently across. Both Self-Reliance and Spontaneity followed his lead and within a few moments found themselves in a thick mist.

'It must be coming up from below,' said Spontaneity. 'It's impossible to see.'

'We don't have to see with our *eyes*,' answered Smith. 'Just keep our minds on what we want.'

After what seemed an eternity of focused concentration, they made step-by-step progress and emerged in the bright sunlight of Prosperity.

□   □   □

'IMAGINE FALLING INTO THE CHASM of professional complacency,' said Self-Reliance. 'For a business to enjoy Good Fortune and then become its own impediment for continuing on to Prosperity is a waste of potential.'

'The chasm reminds me of Superficial Town,' answered Spontaneity. 'How easy it is when you believe you are market leaders ahead of your competitors, to lose sight of your mission and become the issue instead.'

Smith nodded, 'When businesses believe their own propaganda about how successful they are in comparison to other businesses, they no longer consider it necessary to try. Is it any wonder that the majority of businesses do not survive one generation when they view the future as an extension of the past? Yet success is not about comparing ourselves in relation to what others have either done. Success can only be measured in relation to what we ourselves are capable of.'

'Businesses must remind themselves what is important to them,' added Self-Reliance. 'The challenge is that if you ask people why they are doing the work that they are the majority will answer 'to make money of course!' In seeking to chase their pension, rather than their passion, they get by, rather than fulfil themselves.

'Paid work, chosen work and visionary work can be likened to asking three masons working on the same stone what they are doing. The first, who is both disinterested, and bored, replies that the very fact he is sweating in the sun chipping away at some stone clearly shows he is working for money. The second satisfyingly replies that he is carving a statue, which is bringing the sculptor out in him that he always wanted to be. The third replies with a passion in his eyes and a sense of purposeful pride in his heart. For he is building a magnificent cathedral, which though it may not be completed in his lifetime, will be looked upon in awe by generations to come.'

'To be a part of something that you consider has a true goal, instead of seeing it just as a job, is the key to living a rewarding life.' Smith paused. 'But look, I recognise one of those people ahead.'

❏   ❏   ❏

THE AGENTS QUICKENED THEIR PACE and Smith was delighted to see it was Entrepreneur, who having escaped from Superficial with the help of his friend, Influence, was on his way to Deal, a stock-market town close by.

'So, you have made it to Prosperity,' said Entrepreneur after they greeted each other. 'I'm glad to be back myself after my experience of Superficial life. When my friend Influence came looking for me he reminded me to get on with what I was good at, rather than waiting around for something to happen.'

'Then you are lucky to have such a good friend,' said Smith.

'Don't I know it,' replied Entrepreneur.

'I simply reminded you to impress upon others what your strengths and abilities were, so that they would realise it was pointless to hold you back,' put in Influence. 'It would have done no good at all to persuade your captors to let you go through forceful methods, or conditional plea-bargaining.'

'Like saying to a customer, if you do not buy this today, you're going to lose out to someone else,' said Smith.

'Yes, only in this case with all the trumped up charges, the argument was, if you say yes to us we'll give you a reward,' replied Influence. 'The 'yes' of course was to accept that their 'Brand Image' was the very best available, so that we must always buy from them and use their service. Superficial people, of course, believe that advertising campaigns are the only way to build brand image. They won't accept that customers buy because of the feel good factor of purchasing a particular product or service that fulfils what it promises, and continues to always do so. It would have been useless to argue against such fixed thinking so we suggested that we have the opportunity to try all their products and services so that we could tell the world about them.'

'And they liked the idea,' added Entrepreneur. 'So they immediately released me and allowed us to shop at ease. This time of course I did not advocate my own service in preference to theirs. I was careful to keep my own counsel but at the first opportunity we left the awful place. But you can be sure that I will keep my word. For the whole world must be made aware of such awful service!'

'The service challenge for business must be to make every single contact with every customer such a positive experience that the customer perceives the business as excellent,' said Influence. 'This is critical because customers do not buy because of the quality or excellence of a product or service. They buy because of the quality, or excellence, that they *perceive*. And it is their perceptions that will cause them to both purchase a product and recommend the business.'

'Customers must feel good about dealing with a business, to continue to do so,' said Smith. 'No one wants to deal with someone they don't like. Particularly when sharing our desires with a business that promises to fulfil them for us, and then lets us down.'

'Often customers, of course, are reluctant to share their desires anyway in case they are ridiculed because of their lack of knowledge, or are embarrassed for asking a stupid question,' said Self-Reliance. 'That is why it is so critical that the front-line ambassador develops empathy with a customer. The more they get to know a customer, the more they will be able to ensure that the experience the customers perceives will be outstanding.'

'I believe that causing a customer to feel better about dealing with you because of how you deal with the customer is the best,' Influence said. 'It's developing the small tendencies that are important. Like greeting a person with a warm smile and then using their name on subsequently occasions.'

'Which reminds me, we must make our way to Deal for we are meeting with Opportunity there,' said Entrepreneur. 'Will you join us?'

'Right now we are determined to make Service City our next stop,' answered Smith

'And I am sure you will want to make it your last stop when you experience it,' said Entrepreneur. 'Always remember to consider yourself self-employed in everything you do, even if you work for another. Because when you think like that you bring the very best out in yourself.'

'And you bring the best out in others,' added Influence. 'The best entrepreneurs must have management skills and the best managers must think like an entrepreneur. Such leaders are neither timid nor cavalier at whatever they do. They simply do things that

194

they know to be right, have to be done, and are in line with their vision.'

'There's nothing quite like a vision to keep a person on track,' said Smith. 'The most important things my travels have taught me is that you must know where you are going. Otherwise, how will you recognise it when you get there?'

'Or, you end up exactly at the place you always dreaded that you might end up, such as imprisoned in Superficial life listening to Contempt!' said Self-Reliance.

□   □   □

HAVING TAKEN THEIR LEAVE the three agents continued through Prosperity. On the way they first met with Encouragement who confirmed that they were almost there.

'Continue taking one step at a time and the success of your journey is assured,' he said. 'Without the obstacles that you have had to overcome you would feel little satisfaction in reaching Prosperity.'

'Now that we are here whatever complaints we might have had are forgotten,' said Smith.

'Of course, but complaints are not a bad thing when they are viewed as a sign that something is not quite right. When the body has a complaint, for example, it indicates that health is suffering. Indeed the citizens of Service City consider a complaint as an opportunity to build relationships. In treating co-workers as customers, for example, a business there will review its whole customer ethos if it considers that its own people may have cause to complain about anything. For such a business understands that de-motivated ambassadors will find it hard to be motivated in what they do.'

'I understand that the River of Insults lies just before Service City,' said Spontaneity. 'Does everyone have to cross it each time they enter?'

'Everyone does, but it gets easier each time simply because you become impervious to it. Someone who is new to Prosperity and wants to enter the City is more prone to having their thinking tested than another who knows what to expect. For, whatever we expect is right. If you think you can't do something, then you are as right as if you think you can. For whatever outcome you believe will happen, you manifest for yourself. The important factor is do not think of reasons why something can't be done, just find a way to do it.

'Above all don't panic no matter what, even if your head goes under. Just think to yourself that you will never give up and keep trying until you win through. Remember this though. Whatever someone thinks of you is none of your business. You cannot get inside their mind and change their thinking. Only they can do that to themselves. What's important is what you think of yourself, for this is what will ultimately determine your success. Believe you will succeed.'

❑   ❑   ❑

NEXT THEY MET WITH TOLERANCE who, despite being absorbed in what he was doing, took the time to greet and talk with them.

'You will learn that one of the key factors of success in Service City is the ability to get on with other people. To do so, it is important to like people. But you cannot like people if you do not like yourself because then you will be impatient with yourself and thus be impatient with others.

'We cannot communicate more than what we are. If we are impatient for someone to make a decision, then that is what we will communicate, even without words. Thus the customer always knows when the person they are speaking to, either on the phone, or, face to face, is rushing them.

'Human error exists and mistakes happen, and those employers who patiently take the time to explain what is required so that the mistake is not repeated, get the best out of their ambassadors. To reprimand without explanation is not in the interests of the ambassador, the customer, or the growth of the business. People like to know that decisions are made fairly. In that way they can be open about their mistakes and feel accountable for what they do.'

□   □   □

AFTER TOLERANCE THEY MET WITH RELIABILITY who informed them that news of their imminent arrival had already reached the city.

'Everyone has heard of you because you are doing what you have said you would do right from the start. Consistent performance is what the Founder, Customer, desires in business more than anything else. And consistent, high level performance is what every business in the city strives for. It is considered the essential competitive advantage for any business seeking to set the global service standard of excellence within their industry.

'In that way, the Customer can enjoy zero defects within the realm. Providing better-than-excellent service makes the difference between real champions and the also-rans. So when you consider that the number of your repeat customers is in direct proportion to the consistency of your service, always ensure that you never let people down. A consistently *unreliable* friend cannot be a true friend by definition. If you cannot rely on your friends, then whom can you rely on? To be a friend to Customer you must be reliable for it is the best way to build a trusting relationship.'

□ □ □

FINALLY, THEY MET WITH KINDNESS who, full of praise for how they had overcome all of their challenges in order to arrive where they were now, shared with them how consideration leads to reward.

'Under the Law of Contract, there must be a form of consideration agreed between the parties for it to be binding. Without consideration specific performance of the contract cannot be enforced. Consideration is the key that makes it meaningful. But take any interaction between two people, be it husband and wife, doctor and patient or customer and business. Without consideration what meaning does the relationship have? None-at-all. When people are inconsiderate towards each other there is always a consequence. And you can be sure that pain will be involved.

'Being considerate to others is more than treating them as you would like to be treated. It means more than feeling sympathy for their problems and more than wanting to make them feel good. It involves the sincere empathy of putting yourself in their shoes, making them feel good because you are seeing things from a slightly different perspective. It is with this clear thinking that you are able to assist them with what they want and provide the solution that will make a difference. Choosing to serve another willingly is being considerate.

And such consideration brings greater reward than you would expect.

'The Law of Service promises that you will always be rewarded in life, in exact proportion to the value of your service to others. The Law of Secret Service, however, promises that you will always receive in life, greater-than-expected rewards in consideration for how you have treated others. Such rewards may not always come from where you thought, or at the time you hoped. But they will *always* come and will *always* be greater-than-expected.'

❑   ❑   ❑

SHORTLY AFTER THEIR INITIAL ENCOUNTERS in Prosperity, the agents saw its shining Capital: Service City. Across their path, however, lay a fast rushing river.

'That must be the River of Insults and our final obstacle,' said Smith. 'We just have to cross it and we have reached our destination.'

'It looks deeper than I imagined,' said Spontaneity.

'Remember that we must believe we will succeed in crossing it,' said Smith. 'Our imagination is at our disposal to find the way towards our dreams. It is not there for our disposal of them. It can't be that deep, so long as we keep our heads up high, and it is certainly not wide. Come on, we'll be across it in no time at all.'

Almost as soon as they entered the strong current, each agent began to have serious panic attacks about holding their own.

'Come on, you lazy good for nothing!' Self-Reliance thought he heard Smith shout scornfully.

'What did you say?' he shouted back, but Smith did not hear over the shout that he believed he heard Spontaneity make.

'Your worthless vision will kill us all, you fool!'

'What?' shouted Smith.

'You're nothing but a nuisance with all your stupid ideas that no one's interested in!' Spontaneity could have sworn Smith shouted in response to his cry for help when he lost his footing.

'Let him drown, that's all he's good for!' he heard Self-Reliance yell at him as he just managed to keep his head above water.

'Why are you saying cruel things?' Spontaneity spluttered.

Seeing his friend sink, Smith turned back to help and Self-Reliance realised that the River of Insults was distorting their shouts. 'Panic is affecting our thinking,' he thought to himself. 'Trying to stop us with meaningless insults.'

Reaching the others Self-Reliance linked arms with them and they inched their way to the other side. As they did so the noise abated until all that could be heard were affronted whisperings.

'That was awful!' cried Spontaneity.

'What a torrent of abuse,' said Smith. 'Panic was trying to swallow us up so close to accomplishment our mission. What we allow ourselves to listen to can be our very undoing!'

'Learning to be impervious to those who are intent on pouring scorn on our endeavours is one thing,' said Self-Reliance. 'But how alarming to think how quickly we began to misunderstand each other when we are close to losing everything!'

'Reaching your destination builds trust in yourself, yet can only ever be the beginning,' said Smith. 'The building of trust is a continuous process. We must learn to fully trust ourselves for trustworthiness builds trust towards others. When there is trust, insults no longer instil panic.'

'Whereas constructive criticism can be a useful guidance, insults are spawned from jealousy, envy, anger and distrust – all emotions that it is possible to drown in,' said Self-Reliance

'There is one good thing though,' said Spontaneity having got his breath back. 'I suppose that the day people stop insulting you, or saying things about you behind your back, is the day you've stopped growing!'

'Well, it's certainly true that successful mainstream businesses are always current news!' laughed Self-Reliance.

◻   ◻   ◻

AS THEY WALKED FROM THE RIVER BANK toward the city they saw the gatekeeper, Trustee, come out to meet them.

'Welcome!' he said smiling warmly. 'It's great to see that you have arrived. Many crossing that river forget their reason for travelling here in the first place.'

Realising that Trustee was asking, in a polite way, to see his Charter, Smith handed it to him. 'I stand to deliver better-than-excellent service and my friends are with me,' said Smith.

'When you walk your talk, you have no need to declare it to the world, because the world can see for itself.' said Trustee. 'Your values are so clear to see that *I* have no need of proof. That Charter is yours to remind *you* about what you stand for. You are free to enter Service City, for you have already paid the price of success. And you have paid it in advance, which is the only way it can be made.'

◻   ◻   ◻

REACHING WHAT HAD BEEN such an important goal for him left Smith lost for words. Deep down he had a confidence that he had not experienced before. It stemmed from a sense of achievement for having successfully accomplished his mission, despite his trials and tribulations.

He believed that everything he had gone through had been worth it because the value of his self-worth had risen immensely. He had done it! He would now enjoy the rewards of his journey but at the same time he would begin to devise new goals and new plans, all within the framework of his mission.

For the meaning of true success was not where you were at, but in which direction you are going. Success is the *continuous* accomplishment of planned objectives that are worthwhile to the individual. Success itself does not lie in the achievement of the goal, although that is what the State of Mediocrity would consider success. Instead it lies in the journey towards the goal.

Success is a journey. It is the result of a change in thinking, attitudes and new habits acquired during that journey. True success is having belief in yourself and accepting that it is just another name for your unlimited power. 'Yes,' Smith said as he voiced his thoughts. 'True success bears no relation to the person you are before you embark upon its journey. It's your potential to be the person you can become and *will* become when you make a definite resolution.'

◻   ◻   ◻

UPON ENTERING THE CITY, Smith and his friends were met by Agents, Care and Respond, who took them to the very same hotel that Independence had recommended. On the way Care and Respond volunteered details about the service ethos that was prevalent in the city.

'Delighting our Founder, Customer, is considered the only strategy that works here,' said Care. 'Here business leaders ensure that what they stand for and their strategy for delivering it are articulated to all of their ambassadors. Customer doesn't care how much you know, until he knows how much you care, so it is important that your service strategy is clear and concise, well understood and internalised by everyone in the business.'

'Peace of mind is what Customer wants and is willing to pay for it and support businesses that have clearly indicated by their actions that they have Customer's best interests at heart,' said Respond. 'Customer wants security, integrity and the assurance that if there is a problem it will be handled at no extra cost. Customer wants credible service, not hidden agendas or charges, get out clauses and hard sell methods. If Customer chooses to buy products Customer wants them to do what they promise and be reliably safe. With any professional services, such as medical, legal or financial, Customer wants them to be free from liability and kept confidential. Customer always wants to be kept informed as to delivery time for what has been chosen.'

'But you are talking about the Founder,' said Self-Reliance. 'Businesses will be obliged to treat Customer with the utmost respect because he is the Founder. So I must ask, is everyone treated in the same way?'

'Here every customer is considered a Founder, and without exception,' said Respond. 'Business acknowledges that without customers their company would be flounder before it was even founded. Everyone is made to feel special because, above all, everyone of us wants to feel valued. But let me tell you the story when Customer first came here, long before there was a city.

'Years ago there was just a small town here populated by well-to-do people living in Prosperity. One of the shops was a well-established patisserie. The shop only sold expensive, high-quality products and the customers were largely upper-class families in the town. One day a poor scruffy-looking youth entered the shop and asked for one of the delicious looking cakes on display in the window. It was very unusual for such a bedraggled person to shop in such a proud establishment, and the young assistant who waited on him was uncertain at first how he ought to respond to his request. Finally, the assistant wrapped up the cake. When he was about to hand it over, however, the owner of the shop appeared and stopped him. "Just a moment," he said, "let me attend to that." The owner, who had created the cake, took the package from the assistant and presented it to the customer. As he received the money from the scruffy man, he thanked him with very courteous words and then went round the counter to politely open the door for him.

'Puzzled, the young assistant asked the owner, "Sir, why did you wait on him yourself? You've never done that before. It's always one of us, or the cashier, who handles the sales."

The owner nodded and replied, "That's right, but that particular customer was special. We should be truly grateful that he came in today."

"But what's so special about him, sir?" the young assistant asked.

"Our regular customers are all well-to-do people. There's nothing unusual about them buying our products. But that young man wanted that cake so badly that he probably spent everything he had just to buy it.

Shouldn't we be grateful to such a customer? That's why I decided to serve him myself. As a businessman, nothing pleases me more than his kind of patronage. It was as though he was giving himself a reward for something and he chose my product and service to fulfil it."

'You see, I was that young assistant,' said Respond. 'And that day I learned a valuable lesson on what business is all about. The confectioner knew the real joy of business. For him, the customer's worth did not depend on his social status or wealth or even the size of his purchase. Both a business and its ambassadors' greatest pleasure are surely in being able to satisfy customer's needs, and they ought to be grateful for every opportunity to do so.

'As for the scruffy youth, I learned later that it was Customer himself and he had indeed been rewarding himself for having chosen to leave the State of Mediocrity behind, seek Good Fortune through the release of his potential, and arrive here. It was also the last few coins he had in the world and he considered rewarding himself for his personal effort as vital for his future success. I remember he told me much later that, "If we cannot even praise ourselves for the achievement of our goals, then what little value do we assign to ourselves? For if we do not believe that what is important to us warrants reward, then in our own eyes we may as well be worthless."'

Respond paused before adding, 'That, of course, was quite a few years ago now, but it was because of Customer's experience that he resolved to become a leading advocate of better-than-excellent service.

'As Founder of Service City, he wanted to ensure that all the secrets of service would be applied and never forgotten, as they have been in other States outside of Prosperity. So he founded the Agency that would compile the secret service that would help business achieve greater-than-expected rewards for what they did. The Agency, of which we are all operatives, is essential to the success of Service City and Prosperity.

'The Agency realised that many businesses struggled with the paradox of providing service while making money at the same time. After all, the usual excuse in business for doing without it is that service is a costly exercise. But the reality is that greater profitable reward is a result of providing an improved service.

'It is the duty of business, of course, to make a profit. Otherwise a business cannot be in business, and it is being either philanthropic or just indulging in a hobby. Business must furthermore fulfil needs because any business that doesn't, cannot be termed a business. But when service in relation to fulfilling needs and wants, is the main focus, with proper care paid to overheads and profit margins, ambassadors develop the attitude that they are helping customers by what they do. In so doing they open the way to personal growth, for at work you produce something, but in service you *become* someone.

'The Agency believes that the primary purpose of business is to provide service. Profit is the reward received for satisfying customer needs and wants. So if a business desires more reward it simply has to improve its service performance. In doing so it is creating a fulfilling work environment for its ambassadors and a welcoming, reliable and credible establishment for its customers.'

☐   ☐   ☐

ARRIVING AT THE AGENCY HOTEL, Smith noticed the charter that read:

A customer is the most important person to ever enter our hotel. Though they may not be dependent on us; we are dependent on them.

Receptionist greeted the new guests with a warm smile and immediately led them to a pleasant seating area, offered them some complimentary refreshment and took brief check-in details from them. Asking to be excused for a few moments, she soon returned with a colleague from guest relations to take them to their rooms when a familiar face approached Smith.

'It's good to see you again,' Support said. 'And good to see you in much finer spirits than when we first met in Procrastination during my visit to the State Mediocrity.'

For just a moment Smith did not recognise the person that had helped him when he most needed it.

'Of course!' he said. 'If it were not for you I would probably have lost my ambition to leave Apathy behind.'

'You were identified as a perfect operative,' replied Support. 'You carried so much frustration with you that your only hope was to take the action that you, your family and your colleagues thought so drastic at the time. Indeed we must each take our frustration as an indication that we must do what is important to make the necessary changes in our lives.'

'Well, I've certainly done that,' said Smith. 'My frustration was more of a blessing in disguise than I realised.'

'And now that you are here, I would like to be of further service to you,' said Support. 'As soon as I heard that you had arrived I came over from the Agency Bank to meet with you.'

'I appreciate it, but why me?' asked Smith.

'Well,' said Support, 'when the Agency Bank invests, the basis of our criteria is a person's character, for we believe if you invest in character, what better collateral could there be? No document can ever replace integrity, no matter how well worded.'

'You want to invest in me?' enquired Smith.

'You and your team in fact,' replied Support. 'The Agency has followed your progress with interest, having spoken with Accountability, Probity and Innovate, even our operative currently advising in the State of Limbo, Attentive. You have evaluated your motives and know what is important to you. Enthusiasm, Persistence and Discipline have reported that you are more than what they could hope for and indeed exceeded their expectations. I understand from Intuition that you have learned to listen and Inspiration told me that you have a noble mission supported by values. And, as a team, I hear that you have developed your strategy and customer ethos. What more could an investor want? Other than Opportunity and he has already confirmed that he will meet with us as often as you wish.'

Stunned, Smith and his colleagues just looked at each other. What Support had said made everything fall into place and be worthwhile. The three of them had shared so much together in their journey to Prosperity that, even though they were at the brink of realising all of their dreams, they found it hard to believe.

'Such rewards for my endeavours did not seem *possible* when I first started out,' said Smith. 'Yet, the *possibilities* that now exist are endless. Meeting up with Self-Reliance and working with Spontaneity has changed my outlook on life. I came in search of how to give better-than-excellent service and received greater-than-expected reward!'

'There is one thing more, said Support. 'Everything you have learned by undertaking your mission to reach here makes you, under the strict criteria of the Agency, a seasoned operative.

'And, because from today you will be applying our customer ethos, you are now eligible to join our Secret Service. Welcome to Service City, Agent Smith!'

<<< AGENT SMITH FILE NOTE >>>

1. Successful service is founded on personal commitment.

2. Artificial procedures cannot replace attentive service.

3. Think like a self-employed entrepreneur, not a hired hand.

4. Being reliable is builds trusting relationships.

5. Believe that what is important to you, brings reward.

6. Never discriminate because of title or status.

7. Customers know more about your service than you do.

8. Personal involvement brings a sense of purpose into life.

9. The world clearly sees when you walk your talk.

Epilogue

THE VIEW FROM THE TERRACE was spectacular and so was the Service. It was consistently the case at Agency Hotel. But today was made even more special, because of an anniversary celebration.

'For me, the best thing about living in Prosperity this past year has been living *without* your frustration.' said Mrs Smith. 'And to have the children at a school that encourages consideration for others.'

'And encourages them to develop their potential. I always wanted to send them to a school where children are taught how to succeed, rather than how to get by. And to understand that attaining position through meritocracy is more fulfilling than by Superficial means,' replied Agent Smith.

'Don't mention Superficial, it'll make me lose my appetite!' Self-Reliance quipped as he sat down. 'Though that reminds me, we received a message today from a former travelling companion.'

'Impulsiveness?' asked Smith.

'The very same, except he has changed his name to Prepared since recently leaving the State of Chaos, and is now working towards Prosperity. Currently, he is in the Zone of Enterprise with a former bankrupt, who has successfully left Discontent behind him.'

'Here I am,' said Spontaneity. 'With good news! Customer has just awarded us with his loyalty for another year. He really is our best ambassador so we must think of something really special this time to reward *him* for his patronage.'

'And we must also think of something different to reward our own ambassadors for developing the relationships they have with all of our customers,' added Smith. 'The way they convert so many one-time buyers into what will clearly be lifetime partners is excellent! You know, just the other day, I heard our training manager, Vocation, praise some new recruits for treating their first customers like lifetime customers that bought from us everyday!'

'Formerly having been Redundant proved a valuable experience for Vocation, because he has so much empathy for everyone,' said Self-Reliance. 'He believes in the importance of personal development as a precursor for learning how to give better-than-excellent service, and exemplifies his beliefs with his own performance towards his trainees. He literally treats them like his best customers.'

'Praises as well as appraises them!' said Spontaneity.

'Then let's raise a glass to our customers' health, both external and *internal*,' concluded Agent Smith. 'They are the reason Communication Unlimited exists!'

◻   ◻   ◻

TURNER

COLIN

Swimming with Piranha Makes You Hungry

INTERNATIONAL BESTSELLER

Highly Recommended *Financial Times*

Brilliant! *Daily Mail*

Swimming with Piranha makes you Hungry is a unique book humorously illustrated and packed with priceless advice – essential facts to enjoy life more, work less and *have more money!*

Discover powerful practical secrets to simplifying life. Know the Seven Proven Laws vital for gaining wealth.

This book is *guaranteed* to improve the quality of your life; and *increase* your disposable income!

TURNER

COLIN

Y Not - entrepreneurial thinking
PASSION WITH INTEGRITY

How 2 - innovative decisions
CREATIVITY WITH ACTION

4 You - true communication
SIMPLIFYING SITUATIONS

PEOPLE BUY BUSINESS BOOKS,
YET ARE *TOO* BUSY TO READ THEM!

These powerful Little Books offer Dynamic Practical Ideas &

Thought-Provoking Concepts in an accessible format.

A must for everyone in business.
THE SCOTSMAN

TU_{COLIN}RNER

Passion v Pension

DEVELOPING CORPORATE ENTREPRENEURSHIP

Every proactive organization had its origins in
entrepreneurship, yet the originating passion
is too often lost.

Re-instilling the spirit of entrepreneurship into skilled
management is the most effective way to reassure all
stakeholders, re-energize leaders and re-cultivate the
reward of profitable growth.

This book is the definitive guide to achieving that.

- The 10 Principles of Entrepreneurial Leadership
- The 10 Practices of Entrepreneurial Leadership
- Sustain Change with 6 Core Dynamics
- Use the 1% Solution to generate growth

*'Articulates much needed practical and effective
concepts essential for future business success'*
Roger Leek, Group HR Director, Fujitsu Services

'Turner directs with timely advice'
Shingo Miyake, NIKKEI, Japan

'A source of inspiration – read it!'
Frank Boyd, Head of Creative Dept., BBC

TURNER
COLIN

Made for Life

INTERNATIONAL   BESTSELLER

One of the classic tales of wisdom
***Made for life* is both profound and extraordinary.**

This self-psychotherapy masterpiece provides simple

answers to complex questions…

that *everyone* asks of themselves.

'A unique book and most of all it delivers
a very important message. You will love it'
URI GELLER

'I doubt very much whether anyone's life
will remain unchanged after reading it'
HERE'S HEALTH

'A profound, contemplative story'
WAYNE DYER

'If you are looking for answers in your life –
this little book speaks volumes'
STUART WILDE

COLIN TURNER

The Teachings of Billionaire Yen Tzu

Volumes I & II

"Hooks like a thriller you can't put down!"
Time Out

The Teachings of Yen Tzu shakes the very pillars of modern thinking and practice. With esoteric secrets, enlightening stories and insightful wisdom, its provocative lessons present a forgotten yet powerful alchemy for meaning, purpose and prosperity.

"As I am convinced the key to long-term success is a secure philosophical and ethical background, I was delighted to read this book"
Sir John Harvey-Jones

- Learn the Secrets of the Great Moguls and Mandarins.
- Each volume has six insightful lessons
- Learn how to be in the right place at the right time
- Learn how to achieve more while doing less
- Learn how Infinite Patience brings Immediate Results.
- Learn how to realize Desires, while needing nothing.

TURNER
COLIN

to make a difference

THE BOOK THAT CHANGES EVERYTHING

This powerful book reveals the proven keys and
universal laws to ensure success with a practical plan.

Understand	The Success Instinct
Know	The Determinants
Release	The Potential
Draw	The Blueprint
Take	The Action
Follow	The Guide
Realise	The Change

THE RIGHT BOOK FOR RIGHT NOW:
THE BLUEPRINT TO GET TO THE RIGHT PLACE

**For all book orders and bulk discount terms
please email: success@colinturner.com
or visit: www.colinturner.com**